THE

Meal Deal

the
Meal Deal

Blaze Your Own Trail to a
Healthier Eating Lifestyle

To Laura,
Happy Meal Planning!
With Love,
Lisa

Lisa Kiersky Schreiber

BOOKLOGIX®
Alpharetta, GA

ISBN: 978-1-61005-974-9 – Paperback
eISBN: 978-1-61005-975-6 – ePub
eISBN: 978-1-61005-976-3 – mobi

Library of Congress Control Number: 2020923110

Printed in the United States of America   1 0 1 8 2 0

☺This paper meets the requirements of ANSI/NISO Z39.48-1992 (Permanence of Paper)

Photography by Louie Favorite

To Scott, my laugh factory and favorite dinner companion.

An hour of planning can save you ten hours of doing.
—Dale Carnegie

I love it when a plan comes together.
—John "Hannibal" Smith, *The A-Team*

CONTENTS

INTRODUCTION

Food is an important part of a balanced diet.
—Fran Lebowitz

Eating out has become a staple in American culture. Who doesn't enjoy a good meal cooked by someone else? But it has become all too common these days, and Americans are longing for a better way to handle meals. For a way out of overload and into simplicity.

As packaged, ultraprocessed foods have become mainstream, so have studies showing that these foods are not good for us. Combined with dining out, an overconsumption of processed foods is leading to an obesity epidemic (a recent study showed that 42 percent of Americans could be obese by 2030, which may increase health costs by up to $550 billion; Brown, 2012), not to mention an increase in diabetes and heart disease. Cancer may even be linked to our eating habits.

Changing the way we eat has never been more critical.

A slew of evidence indicates that it's important to be aware of what and how we're eating, but many of us don't know how to make significant changes to our food habits. I'd like to throw an essential, and often overlooked, ingredient into the mix: meal planning. It sounds simple, but it may not feel easy. Without a plan, it's far too tempting to reach for fast, less optimal choices. For example, we eat out too often or haphazardly throw together meals day by day with packaged products, which can lead to frustration or boredom and often drive us back to eating out.

A recent CNBC article stated that "90 percent of Americans don't like to cook—and it's costing them thousands each year" (Martin, 2017). I'm speculating here, but I'd venture to say that part of the problem for people is more a lack of planning than it is a pure hatred of cooking. And even if they truly despise cooking, it could be that the meals they're attempting to make are tedious, time-consuming, bland, or not as enticing as eating out.

But what if cooking with real food was something you looked forward to as much as eating out? What if you looked at your menu for the week and couldn't wait to actually cook those meals?

You've probably heard the proverb, "Give a man a fish, and you feed him for a day. Teach a man to fish, and you feed him for a lifetime." Today's equivalent might be, "Give someone a meal plan, and they eat healthier for a week. Teach someone how to meal-plan, and they eat healthier for a lifetime."

I'm guessing that the majority of you have read other diet or meal-planning books, but the problem is, no one else knows your habits and lifestyle. Most meal-planning books are little more than cookbooks with a few planning tips thrown in. You're given some recipes and maybe a few ideas for how to plan out a few days at a time, but then quickly you're on your own again. This translates into making extra grocery-shopping trips or agonizing over which fast food restaurant to visit. Irritation sets in, and the endless cycle begins again the next week.

Dozens of websites are dedicated to providing you with weekly meal plans, for a fee of course. But I find that these books and websites are like a diet plan. They work for a short period of time, but, as is the case with dieting, the weight eventually comes back. In following someone else's plan, you eventually lose interest, and because you don't know how to do it yourself, you give up and your old eating habits kick in again. Though these resources can prove helpful, they are limited in their scope.

For years, I waded through cookbooks and other types of books, hoping to find the magic solution to the mystery that is meal planning. I never found one, so I slowly created my own system instead. It's a method I've honed and used myself for over eighteen years. So while this is the first edition for you, it's more like the tenth or fifteenth version for me. If you stop looking for shortcuts and put in a little time and effort, meal planning can be life changing. With the right tools, you can build the skills you need to fend for yourself in the kitchen. Together, we'll also develop simple methods that can lead to a lifetime of healthier eating habits. But you bear sole responsibility for planning your meals. And, hopefully, that will feel empowering rather than intimidating by the end of our time together.

I spent years in the dieting and weight loss/weight gain trenches. And then I discovered and employed tools to dig myself out. Whether or not you're currently, or have ever been, on the diet carousel, cooking at home more often with real, whole foods is *the* most important thing you can do for yourself if you want to have healthier eating habits. Start here, and you're already on the right path. And meal planning is the first and biggest step toward putting you in control. Using resources you already have, *The Meal Deal* will simplify how you eat, and I don't know anyone who couldn't use a little simplification in their life. How appetizing does it sound to be the boss of your food world?

Meal planning has been essential to my own personal quest to lose weight by eating healthier. Many years ago, I joined one of the most popular weight-loss programs with the goal of losing twenty-five pounds. I quickly found that the trick for me was to plan out everything I was going to eat each day, which turned into meal planning every week. In nine months, I was down to the size I wanted to be. But I've signed up for the same program twice in my lifetime and also tried the low-carb thing on several occasions, and even though I did lose about twenty-five pounds each time, I eventually ended up gaining at least ten to fifteen back. And that's when I decided not to be a slave to yo-yo dieting for the rest of my life.

However, the meal-planning techniques I developed through my dieting experience proved invaluable, because my "new normal" has allowed me to remain at a weight I've learned to be comfortable with for quite some time. Along with learning to love and appreciate my body for what it can do, having meal-planning strategies in place has made my new normal something I'm proud to have in daily life. I may always tweak things here and there and play with new ideas, but there's absolutely nothing as reassuring as knowing I can be in control and trust myself around food. Even more than that, I have come to love, and rely on, knowing I have the ingredients on hand to make a delicious, healthy dinner every night. This approach has helped me not only feed my body, but feed my soul.

In fact, as infrequent as it is, I feel lost when I don't know what's for dinner. Sure, I slip every now and then. But because I rely on engrained meal-planning techniques, I don't beat myself up when I do occasionally stumble. I just start over. I am not a trained chef and have no background in the food industry (other than working in a few restaurants as a teenager). I'm just someone who likes food—a lot. And though I'm no longer as scrupulous about planning everything I'm going to eat all day, I know that my meal-planning skills will keep me on track. I have become a tremendous foodie and decent cook because I've enjoyed the learning process in the kitchen. I haven't seen it as a chore in years. It's just pure fun for me, and quite frankly, I find it very relaxing and cathartic.

Now, I'm not promising you will feel the same way about cooking. But I have a feeling that once you master meal planning, you might not look at it as such an undesirable thing to do, especially when you see the tremendous benefits. And you may discover a joy for cooking you never knew you had, or rediscover one that has fallen by the wayside.

Another reason I turned to meal planning occurred in 1999 when I was diagnosed with Crohn's disease. Crohn's is an inflammatory bowel disease that can cause symptoms such as diarrhea, weight loss, severe abdominal pain, and malnutrition—all of which I experienced. The disease ended up having a profound impact on my eating habits. Once my symptoms were managed, I talked to several people who said they had used nutrition to control their flare-ups. I was determined to do anything in my power to wean myself off the heavy-duty drugs I had to take, so I did a ton of research and learned that ultraprocessed foods were to blame for a lot of intestinal issues, and, in general, they were just not as nutritious as whole foods. So I started cooking more with less-processed ingredients.

To my astonishment, after a while, I was able to come off all the drugs I was on and (knock on wood) have been in remission for almost twenty years. This is remarkable because Crohn's is usually chronic, and dealing with flare-ups is a lifelong endeavor. I have no scientific evidence that eating more whole foods and cutting back on the ultraprocessed options placed me into remission. But I decided there was absolutely no harm in giving this way of eating a try to see if it made a difference. And what a difference I've noticed, indeed!

The Meal Deal is a culmination of my many years of meal-planning experience and is intended to be a guide to changing your eating habits through meal planning. This is not the only way to do it; it is how I do it. So, I will also provide alternate suggestions to get your own creativity flowing. You don't have to do this all at once either. Start slowly, and you will quickly build momentum because you'll see such benefits. But I do believe that meal planning is a significant tool that can lead you toward control over your food life.

Most other books and diets tell you exactly what to eat. But here you get to be in charge. You'll be the one picking the recipes because you know what you and your family like, but I'll give you a framework, guide you, and cheer you on.

This book is for people who want to gain control over their food lives but feel overwhelmed and stuck. After reading *The Meal Deal*, you'll be able to simplify how you eat on a daily basis and have solid action steps to keep you from feeling paralyzed by the insane amount of conflicting information thrown at you. And you'll learn to develop habits to make this new information stick.

What's Your Why?

During my Precision Nutrition (PN) experience, I was given the task of listing Five Whys to get to the core of why I wanted to do something. When I apply this to healthier eating, here's my response:

1. Why do I want to eat healthier? Because I want to age well, stay at a healthy weight, and possibly stave off diseases.
2. Why are those things important to me? Because it makes movement easier and day-to-day life more enjoyable.
3. Why does it matter if my day-to-day movement is better? Because it helps me feel better physically and mentally and allows me to carry out day-to-day tasks with less effort.
4. Why does it matter if I feel better physically and mentally? Because when I feel well, I spend more time realizing my potential and making a contribution to the world.
5. Why does it matter if it helps me give back to the

world? Because feeling like I have a purpose is what keeps me going every day.

So when things start to feel tough, I refer back to my Fifth Why, and it reminds me why it's important for me to eat healthier overall, and this reminder keeps me going.

Have you ever thought about "why" you do something? Even though the "why" or purpose of it all is too big of a topic to take on in one tiny book about meal planning, applying your "why" to things can help you keep going when you feel like giving up or you stray off track. I try not to assume, but because you bought this book, I assume one of your big "whys" is to eat healthier for a lifetime. Within that, you probably have hundreds of even bigger "whys." For example:

- Because I want to feel good physically and mentally for as long as possible.
- Because I want to prevent diseases.
- Because I want to be around to play with my grandkids.
- Because I want to age well and be able to take care of myself for as long as possible.

So when you're learning new knife skills or organizing your pantry, remember your deeper motivations for eating healthy at home.

I'm not telling you exactly what to eat or setting limits for you. I know this is really different than the books you've read or things you've heard on food and health. So it may feel scary or you may question, why bother? Maybe you think the more complicated it is, the better it must work. But what have you got to lose by letting go of those restraints and giving something new a try?

I hope your biggest takeaway from this book will be newfound clarity about your food lifestyle so healthier eating becomes a way of life instead of a short-term endeavor. But if you try something from the book and find it doesn't work for you or resonate with you, don't waste your time trying to make it fit into your lifestyle. But do ask yourself *why* it doesn't work for you (and be honest and nonjudgmental about the answer) and consider whether something else might work instead.

My grand vision is to have you cooking at home using mostly whole foods at least 80 percent of the time. Why 80 percent? Because life is way too short to miss out on tasty foods we grew up loving—at least some of the time. Trust me, no one enjoys pizza, hamburgers, or any icy-cold fountain Coke more than I do. And chocolate? Fuggedaboutit! I am only human after all. But because my normal day consists of eating mainly foods I've cooked at home using quality ingredients, I don't feel bad—or really even think about—the other 20 percent of the time. I know that I'm at least filling my body and soul with nourishing foods the majority of the time.

Because of meal planning, my husband and I sit down together almost every night for a home-cooked meal. We look forward to the time together. I've planned our meals and done the grocery shopping, and my dry-erase board has a list of meals we're sharing for the week. Similar to the daily specials you might see in front of a restaurant, writing them out on the dry-erase board makes me feel like they are something special and a treat to look forward to. It also gives my husband a look at his choices for the week, which he absolutely loves.

Even if you are on a diet plan or have specific weight-loss goals, these cooking-at-home fundamentals can set up your home environment for success.

Along with offering meal-prep tips, I'm also going to ask you to practice self-acceptance and self-compassion. I say *practice* because these attributes don't come naturally to a lot of us and can often be a root cause of many of our eating challenges. If these skills come naturally to you, I genuinely say kudos to you and keep doing what you're doing (and maybe you can pass along some of that confidence to the rest of us).

I will never be perfect at any of this, and I have spent many years striving to accept my food struggles and my body. I have come a long way in finding peace, knowing that doing the best I can is enough sometimes—and when I don't do the best I can, that's okay too. So let's all keep practicing the self-love thing, because it's fundamental to this framework.

What to Expect on *The Meal Deal* Journey

Learn Healthier Eating Habits

"Healthier" doesn't mean increasing your consumption of diet crap or cutting out many of the foods you love. It simply means incorporating more whole foods into your life. Healthier eating will automatically occur as soon as you start planning meals that don't rely on overly processed foods. A reduction in sodium, added sugars, and unhealthy fats will naturally occur from this type of eating, which can lead to weight loss or maintenance, more consistent energy levels, and an overall feeling of well-being. Though I'm not advocating that you never eat out again, I am saying that focusing on overall healthier eating habits (at least most of the time) will go a long way.

You'll also learn that how you eat is as important as what you put in your body. So, we'll discuss awareness techniques you can use whether eating at home or having a meal out.

I'll show you how to create balanced meals that fill your body with the nutrients it needs to survive. No need to count macros or calories. If you create balanced meals, you're likely to get what you need because you have a variety of food on your plate.

Knowing what's for dinner also enables you to make more sensible lunch choices. If, for instance, sandwiches are on the dinner menu, you may opt for a salad or protein-packed option with fewer carbs or white flour (such as another sandwich) for lunch. In contrast, if dinner will be a steak and a salad, a sandwich is a good lunch choice. Then you'll give your body more of a chance to burn the carbs off because you ate them earlier in the day. Meal planning also generates delicious leftovers that can easily be used for lunches. One dish could be used for at least two—maybe three—meals. How about that? Think about the money and calories you'll be saving by not eating lunch out every day.

Develop a Habit-Based Approach

You'll practice making healthier eating a daily habit, but I present this new approach in a simplified way so that you don't feel overwhelmed and give up.

Taking super simple steps every day and practicing

those steps for weeks makes meal planning and cooking at home a habit. And this is important because making something a habit means it becomes an automatic behavior. I call this your "new normal." For me, after years of developing habits, my "new normal" behaviors include cooking at home with real food most of the time and eating out or preparing ultraprocessed foods much less frequently.

At first, you may have to jump back on the "new normal" wagon often, but once you've established a new way of eating, it feels strange when you're not doing it. For example, if I'm on vacation and eating out every night, I go back to my "new normal" as soon as I get home. Consistent and repeated actions create change and growth.

Perform a Kitchen Makeover

A kitchen makeover gives you a clean slate and sets you up with more nutritious items in your pantry and fridge. Whatever surrounds you is what you'll likely reach for. So if you keep healthier options in close proximity, you have a better chance of consuming more nutritionally dense foods. By deciding in advance what foods will stay, which will go, and what needs to be added, you will make conscious decisions about your food environment. And by keeping ultraprocessed foods out of your kitchen, you'll have to make a special effort if you want them, which makes it harder to binge on them.

Stock Your Kitchen Well

Keeping essential items in your kitchen at all times will ensure that you never have to make a last-minute run to the store for missing ingredients. It also makes it a lot easier to prepare a backup meal if your first attempt at a recipe falls apart like a sunken soufflé. I'll suggest items to keep on hand, and you will discover many of your own as you go along. I'll also recommend important cooking utensils to keep in the kitchen and offer good storage methods to promote proficient use of those items. This will allow you to swiftly move through your kitchen and prepare meals efficiently. When you feel confident that you have everything you need to cook and you know exactly where it is, you'll feel less overwhelmed about making meals.

Find Recipes and Know What to Look For

These healthier eating skills will give you a new a lens for evaluating recipes—one that filters out recipes with a lot of ultraprocessed ingredients.

Finding recipes and putting together weekly menus will be your sole responsibility, so I will not offer many recipes (and the ones I will offer are incredibly simple and aimed at helping you get vegetables, lean protein, and whole grains into your diet more easily). As much as I'd like to get to know all of you, I don't know what you like. But I will give you tips on where to look for recipes and what to look for. My tools are a road map to help you find the best options among the plentiful recipe ideas that already exist. This new eye for healthy recipes makes you self-sufficient in the kitchen and eventually a meal-planning guru.

The internet, along with the cookbooks you already

own and maybe a subscription to a great cooking magazine, offers an endless supply of free recipes and is pretty much everything you need to take control of your weekly meal planning. I'll provide you with keys to using magazine and website resources to their best advantage so you can more easily synthesize weekly menu plans from easily available sources.

Create Your Own "Cookbook"

You'll never again forget where you put that delicious recipe you made for dinner last week when you create your own "cookbook" in which to store it. This resource proves invaluable when searching for recipes to put together your weekly menus and will ensure that quick meal planning is always at your fingertips. You'll learn how to set up your "cookbook," as well as how to store recipes you want to try in the future. It will become your go-to first source for including more nutritious recipes in your weekly menu plans.

Design Weekly Balanced Menus

Do you ever watch cooking shows or read magazines and think a dish looks great but sense it's not very practical in terms of a balanced meal? Many times, cooking show dishes don't complement each other. Maybe they're too heavy on the starches, or the entire show is dedicated to desserts. And while magazines give you recipes, they rarely help you make a complete menu. It's up to you to figure out how best to piece together an entire menu plan, a task that can seem daunting.

Taking your new knowledge of what balanced meals

look like, you will eliminate the guesswork, consistently pick dishes that work together, and get more nutritional bang for your buck. Knowing how to create your own plan decreases dependence on any one source. Plus, having your menus spelled out can get you excited about what's for dinner.

Planning out your weekly menus also reduces stress by preventing the "what's for dinner tonight" panic, which often leads to choosing less healthy meals. No more drumming your fingers on your desk in desperation or running to the grocery store or drive-thru last minute because you weren't prepared.

Create a Grocery List to Shop Efficiently

Who wants to spend a lot of time at the grocery store? Spreadsheets and phone apps are a terrific way to itemize your grocery store products, which helps get you in and out faster. And having a list will keep you from wasting money on items you don't need (a.k.a. highly processed packaged foods) or ingredients you thought you'd use but end up throwing away.

Beware, other shoppers might stop you and tell you they're envious of your beautiful, typed list and the way you breeze through the store.

Prepare Meals Like a Pro

You'll learn methods to help you organize the cooking process and reduce your time in the kitchen, which takes the complexity out of your efforts and makes it more likely that you'll keep showing up.

Precook Foods in Your Spare Time

Did you know you can utilize spare time to precook foods to use for quick dinners, backup meals, lunches, and/or snacks? It's so satisfying to open your fridge and see these healthy prepared foods; better choices meet convenience when you think ahead.

Create Backup Meals

Mishaps occur. That's life. But that doesn't mean you must run to the store or order takeout. Your newly stocked kitchen will save the day as you learn to create backup meals with what you have on hand. I'll help you conjure up magic by offering basic backup ideas using ingredients already in your pantry and fridge. This will make you more comfortable with experimenting when things don't go exactly as planned and keep you on track to eat at home instead of instantly choosing a less healthy option.

The Lay of the Land

In each chapter, I'll give you a list of main principles/actionable steps so that you can quickly refer back to them as often as needed. Then I'll elaborate on each of those steps to show you how to make them consistently work for you. I've also included some extra tips just for fun. Finally, at the end of each chapter, I suggest small, habit-based behaviors to reinforce the actionable steps so it becomes easier to maintain your healthier eating lifestyle automatically without overthinking. And then I'll give you a checklist you can use to evaluate how you're doing.

When I was working toward my Precision Nutrition Level 2 certification, I learned how remarkably different we all are in terms of forming habits. And by understanding and respecting these differences, I'm hoping *The Meal Deal* will speak to the part of you that wants to make changes but has realized no one else can give you a prescribed, perfect solution for your unique lifestyle. I offer principles that you can integrate and adapt based on your needs and preferences.

This habit-based approach has already changed at least two lives (mine and my hubby's), and I hope that it can do the same for you. Or at least get you started.

You can read and implement this book and its suggestions in several ways. The first option is slow and steady. You don't move on to the next chapter until you feel confident in the new habits you've already read about. Taking on too much at one time doesn't stick in the long run, but taking small steps and making them habits can work for a lifetime. Because it can take several weeks to form a new habit, I've arranged this book in a particular order so that forming each habit helps you naturally move on to the next one.

The second approach is to read it straight through and take what you will from it. Some people just prefer a faster pace, and once excited about a topic, they push on until they understand fully—and that's good too.

The third strategy is to go all the way through the text once to get a sense of the entire system and then go back chapter by chapter to establish each habit.

Whatever approach you take, I hope *The Meal Deal* will help you get your healthier food lifestyle on track.

Materials for Weekly Meal Plans

- Pen or pencil and paper: to write down your weekly menus
- Internet access (*preferred*): to search for recipes, find helpful websites, and sign up for cooking newsletters
- Cookbooks: to search for recipes and find inspiration
- Large binder or several smaller binders: to start your own cookbook
- Extra binder or file folder: to store recipes to try
- Two sets of dividers (preferably at least one with pockets)
- Clear sheet-protector covers (I prefer heavy-duty, non-glare)
- Lined paper or magnetic pad: to keep a running grocery list (I keep mine near the refrigerator)
- Dry-erase board, chalkboard, or corkboard (*optional*): to display meal plans in the kitchen so everyone will know what's for dinner each week and you'll remember when to thaw or marinate ingredients
- Cooking magazines (*optional*)
- A laid-back attitude: to ensure you have fun with no expectations of perfection

To sign up for free bonus material with information on each chapter, go to lisakschreiber.com/the-meal-deal-book.

* * *

As I was writing this book and because of my own self-discovery process, I came to realize the book had to be about more than just planning meals. Though its main goal is to give you a framework for feeding your body, it's also meant to foster acceptance, love, and compassion for self so you can also feed your soul.

I'm offering a piece of my experience in hopes you can use it to fuel your own journey of growth.

If you're ready to start your journey toward transforming your food lifestyle, head to chapter 1, and let's start with one of the biggest, most important parts of the process: establishing healthier eating habits.

If you need a little more convincing that setting up your home environment is fundamental to establishing a lifetime of healthier eating habits, read on.

Why Bother?
Some Benefits of Meal Planning

Saves Money, Time, and Inches

A 2019 article in *USA Today* said prices at full-service restaurants have jumped 2.7 percent in one year (Meyer). While your grocery bills may increase with meal planning, your dining-out bills will decline exponentially. So if you weigh the overall cost of food consumption in your household, you should find eating at home a lot less expensive in the long run.

Meal planning frees you up to have more time for other things in your life. If you add up the time you currently spend thinking about what's for dinner every night, I bet it will come out to a number higher than you think. But if you were to take twenty minutes one day a week to plan out your menus, you won't have to think about it again for seven days or more. And with your once-a-week trip to the market, you'll be shaving time off grocery store runs or dining-out excursions. This can add up to hours of time you can now spend on things you'd rather be doing. And, yes, cleanup is a lot easier if you eat out, but the benefit of eating a healthier meal at home far outweighs a few dirty dishes. And with some simple tricks, your kitchen doesn't have to look like a tornado twisted through it. I'll show you how cleanup can be a snap.

Here's a statistic that may or may not shock you: one recent study found that 96 percent of restaurant entrées exceed USDA limits for calories, sodium, fat, and saturated fat. Another study found that calorie count, sodium levels, and portion sizes of entrées, sides, and desserts at ten popular fast food chains had "increased significantly" over a thirty-year period (Horovitz, 2012; Elsevier, 2019).

Clearly, restaurants make food taste great by adding lots of sugar, salt, butter, and other ingredients that pack on pounds. This can even be true if you're just ordering a salad. Planning your menus each week can help you with weight control or weight loss. Just by cooking at home more often, you could save a tremendous amount of calories, possibly shrinking your waistline.

And studies show that healthier eating can be beneficial in warding off many illnesses. While using better ingredients to make your meals can sometimes be a little more expensive (though many studies say this isn't the case), spending money on quality foods could certainly keep you from spending a lot more on your future health bills. And that's a *huge* deal!

Meal planning will also help you wean yourself off less nutritious food choices. If you don't keep those foods in your home (if they're not on your grocery list, you won't be buying them), you won't be able to automatically reach for them. You'll have to go out of your way to get them. And, believe it or not, your body will actually begin to crave healthier foods. I experienced that myself and miraculously saw it happen with my husband.

Be the Boss

You get to be in the driver's seat and not allow anyone else to dictate your personal taste. Plus, if you have dietary restrictions (such as celiac disease, heart disease, etc.) and know what foods you need to steer clear of, you can easily skip recipes that call for those foods and better tailor your menus to fit your needs.

Simplify Your Life and Save Your Sanity

Are you overwhelmed when you walk into the grocery store and see hundreds of cereal boxes or salad dressings? A 2016 article in *Business Insider* states that "choosing between too many options can cause decision fatigue, which can lead to worse decisions down the road," and that "an abundance of choices leaves less time to make the right decision" (Gillett). Having a plan before you go to the grocery store narrows your choices, thereby simplifying your life and eliminating a lot of decision-making stress. And by cooking with mostly whole foods, your choices will be even narrower as you select more nutrient-dense options.

Challenge Stereotypes

For all you women out there saying to yourselves, *I refuse to be the little homemaker, tied to the kitchen like my mom or grandmom*, I'd like to turn the tables. Taking control of the eating situation leaves you in charge—not bound to drudgery. Do it for yourself first, and if anyone else happens to benefit from all your hard work, it is just an added bonus. When I started out, I saw cooking as the traditional role of a woman. I was headstrong, so I refused to take on that role for fear of becoming the "little homemaker." But several years into my relationship, I figured out that eating bad food all the time, which we were doing because neither of us wanted to cook, was a lot worse than taking on that role (and I had many extra pounds to prove it).

So I took over. I was going to be in charge of eating what I thought were healthier meals. And if hubby didn't like it, he could fend for himself. If it were up to him, we'd eat tacos and hot dogs for dinner every night. Of course, I consider my husband's likes and dislikes and always ask if he has any preferences, but when I let go of the "homemaker" notion, I had power over my—and, as it turned out, *our*—eating habits. Abandon stereotypes and see this as an opportunity to be in charge. Nothing is antiquated about taking steps toward a healthier food life.

And if you're a guy, embrace the new millennium. Lots of people think that a man who likes spending time at the stove or grill is sexy—just consider Bobby Flay, Tyler Florence, Jamie Oliver, Curtis Stone, Emeril Lagasse, or any other famous male chefs. They are some of the biggest celebrities on television.

Must I Do This Alone?

While celebrity chefs do a phenomenal job of helping you get food on your table, there is no comprehensive, all-encompassing book, magazine, or cooking show that will help you design weekly meal plans, because no one knows what you and your family like to eat but you. So it can feel like you're on your own. But you're not. I'm here to help.

After the Crohn's experience caused me to take a keen interest in food, I saw the real value of nutrition and wanted to use my new insights and enthusiasm to help other people. And that's when I found Precision Nutrition, an online company that helps clients transform their nutrition and fitness lives, as well as mentors fitness and health professionals to become elite coaches. I fell in love with their information, beliefs, and style. PN meshed so beautifully with my new personal food philosophy that I immediately signed up for their Level 1 nutrition certification, where I learned a lot of the science behind nutrition and how the body processes food. But the biggest draw for me was how they coach others to help clients with nutrition and behavior change.

So when they offered their first-ever Level 2 master class, I didn't hesitate to join the yearlong mentorship program, which trains those who want to become coaches themselves. I studied under incredible mentors and followed daily and weekly habits. I turned in my solutions to real case studies and received feedback. This turned out to be a life-changing experience for me, as I developed new skills and saw my own behaviors change. I ended up helping myself as much as anyone, which made me empathetic to the struggles of others and gave me incredible techniques to become a client-centered coach who aims to guide clients instead of just tell them what to do.

I explain my journey so you won't feel alone on yours. At the end of the book, I'll tell you how to get in touch with me if you find yourself needing more guidance, or if you just need a friend to bitch about food with. You can also stay connected and motivated through social media, where other people share their weekly menus to give you inspiration. Or, find my weekly menus online with links to some of the recipes at lisakschreiber.com.

And consider recruiting your friends. Make it a group thing, if you like. Everyone can benefit! Get together with friends and share recipes. Take turns writing out one weekly menu plan with a grocery list and share it. Or have each person write out a plan each week and rotate lists so you always have something new. Try making the meal-planning process a community thing, and you'll always have others to help you out and cheer you on. A social support system is a powerful thing.

If both you and your significant other don't mind cooking, you're in luck. You can share the responsibility. Or if he/she doesn't like to meal plan but likes cooking, you do the menu planning and then take turns making the meals. You can learn the planning process together or just bounce ideas off each other when it comes time to plan your menus. This will make things go quickly, and everyone will be involved.

A Family Affair

Get your kids, spouse, partner, dog, goldfish, and anyone else in your household involved in the planning process each week. This will develop good standards early on. Not only will they take pride in knowing they helped plan the menus, but they'll also look forward to enjoying the meal they picked. And, if you're lucky, maybe they'll even make it themselves (though be prepared for a mess if you're going to let your kids make dinner). You'll also know you all came to a consensus on what to eat. If others are directly involved in helping put together those weekly meal plans, you no longer bear the pressure of making sure everyone is happy with the menu selection.

I tested this theory when my seven-year-old nephew, a notoriously picky eater, came to town. I enlisted him in helping me cook dinner one night. He out-ate me and my husband—something he's never done before—and raved about how good everything tasted. My sister was floored and decided to involve him in their meal-planning efforts.

What's Up with Weekly?

Why do I advocate weekly meal plans as opposed to longer periods of time? Shopping every week allows you to cook with fresh foods without fear of them going bad or losing nutrients. Spoilage is actually a good indication that you're working with more natural, nutritious ingredients. A week is just about the right amount of time before your basil wilts like Oscar the Grouch in a rainstorm and your lettuce starts smelling like a wet dog.

Also, a week is a manageable amount of time and

shouldn't feel too overwhelming. And spending fifteen to twenty minutes a week to plan menus is more realistic than spending several hours to plan for two weeks or a month or more. Plus, if you try planning for longer, you may decide you aren't in the mood to eat whatever you chose two weeks ago. But if you want to plan for longer periods of time, give it a go. You may still want to do your grocery shopping once a week, however, or you risk foods going bad. And you don't want to rely on packaged items at the end of your meal-planning period, because they're not as nutritious.

I make no apologies that meal planning takes a little time. And I admit that I don't always love doing it. But many of us already take the time to exercise, spend time with family, go on vacation, write a book (quite the project), or even have our hair colored (in my case, every four weeks—thanks for passing along those grays, Mom). We make the time to do things we enjoy or know are good for us. If you start to think of meal planning as something that could benefit your health over the short and long term, maybe you'll make the time to do it too.

And take it easy on yourself. I still have weeks when I absolutely dread the thought of going through my recipes, putting together my plan for the week, and hitting the market. Though I know all the friendly people who work there because of my weekly trips, I don't always look forward to making those outings. Sometimes it's not fun or convenient.

However, I will say that once I've completed these things, I am so unbelievably happy knowing that I won't have to step foot in that store for a week and will have at least six or seven healthy dinners (and usually lunches) available to me. It makes it all worthwhile. And, at this point, planning my menus is so ingrained that I can't even imagine not doing it. I would feel completely lost if I didn't have food in the house to make lunch and dinner every day. I can't describe the sense of satisfaction and joy I get from looking at the dry-erase board on my fridge covered with my hand-scribbled meals for the week. My mom loves coming over and raiding my fridge because she knows there will always be something fresh, homemade, and delicious in there. And I love looking in my fridge stocked full of nourishing foods and knowing that I've got tons of delectable options and am doing something great for my body.

If you just can't muster the energy to develop a meal plan one week, don't sweat it. Start over the next day or the following week. Pretty soon, I think you will see such benefits to meal planning that, although you still may not always scream for joy when it comes time to sit down with your recipes, you'll remember the rewards are so great that you'll make the time to do it.

Now, let's dive in with a look at establishing overall healthier eating habits.

Chapter 1

ESTABLISH HEALTHIER EATING HABITS

The only time to eat diet food is while
you're waiting for the steak to cook.

—Julia Child

After my Crohn's disease diagnosis, it took some time to rethink my eating and cut back on ultraprocessed foods, especially since they were convenient and tasted so good. And it in no way happened overnight. It was way more of an organic process. I had to peel back the layers and gradually figure out how to cook, especially with whole foods. I also had to unwrap my personal baggage around food and learn to be mindful of what I was consuming at every meal. I eventually learned that simplicity and awareness are key.

But simple does not always mean easy. For instance, which do you think is a better choice: eating Skittles candy or snacking on an apple? You may want to "taste the rainbow," but I'm willing to bet you already know the answer to that question. However, when that bag of candy is available after a hard day at work or an exercise session, how easy do you think it will be to decide to eat an apple instead? See? Simple, but not easy.

And while food is a basic necessity in life, it's also a source of struggle for many people. A lot is wrapped up in our relationships with food, especially if you've spent years and years dieting.

It can feel complicated and overwhelming, especially when you hear contradictory information about what constitutes a healthier diet. But the truth is, the mainstays of a healthier diet are fairly straightforward. We're just making things more complicated than they need to be. Maximize your intake of whole foods, especially protein, vegetables, and fiber, as they help you fill up faster and stay fuller longer. Not complicated. The food industry does not want you to know that. It's their job to sell more products, so they want to keep you confused and over-whelmed. And they want to make it easier for you to grab their ultraprocessed, convenient offerings because that's how they make money.

Where I think a lot of people get tripped up is when they focus too much on counting macros and/or calories or following the latest fad diet because they read it can lower their cholesterol or help them drop twenty pounds in a month.

After several attempts at dieting, I finally decided I'd had enough. I was tired of following someone else's rules and was ready to see if I could eat healthier entirely on my terms. But I will tell you, it can feel scary and down-right impossible to trust that you don't need rules for how and what to eat, especially if you've fallen into the diet trap for much of your life.

So, before we get to meal planning, we need to start with the foundation of healthier eating habits.

What do I mean by healthier eating habits? First of all, don't freak out—healthier eating does *not* mean you have to become a vegetarian or vegan, or even cut out any of the meals you love. And it absolutely doesn't mean sticking to any kind of low-fat, low-carb, or no-sugar diet. It doesn't even mean eating only organic foods.

To me, healthier eating begins with cooking meals at home more often and using whole foods, not highly processed ones. Whole foods are foods that are unprocessed and unrefined, like vegetables, lean proteins, beans, fruits, whole grains, and herbs and spices. They contain beneficial nutrients, vitamins, and minerals—things your body craves.

In fact, studies show that your body will continue to crave food until you give it what it needs. That's one reason we have an obesity epidemic in this country. We keep eating and eating because our body is telling us we haven't given it the proper nutrition. Start giving it more nourishing foods and you might not feel the need to consume so much. A reduction in sodium, added sugars, and saturated fats will naturally occur when you make the move toward eating more whole foods.

By the end of this chapter, you'll have a simplified view of what to consider each time you sit down for a meal, including methods you can carry with you outside of your kitchen that can help you eat healthier for a lifetime. You'll also know how to pull together balanced meals that cover your nutritional bases.

Here is a list of basic healthier eating principles to keep in mind. I've listed the steps by themselves in a separate box so you can refer back to them as often as you need:

Step 1	Eat mindfully.
Step 2	Consume whole foods as often as possible.
Step 3	Add, don't subtract.
Step 4	Read labels.
Step 5	Balance your meals.

Basic Healthier Eating Principles

Step 1: Eat Mindfully

How you eat is just as—or maybe more—important than what you eat and is a more interesting and fruitful conversation. Mindful eating allows you to notice when you feel hungry and when you're full so you can stop eating earlier. If you're like my husband, you recognize when you're full, and you just stop eating—something that makes me crazy with jealousy. But if you're anything like me, it's a lot harder to do that, especially if something tastes really great or even if there's just food left on the plate in front of you.

I battle with this daily, but I can tell you that the more I practice the following techniques, the more I see changes. I'll never be perfect, but I keep improving all the time. So I focus on becoming more aware and doing a little better at each meal. If you *are* like me, expect these techniques to feel like a struggle for a while, and let go of perfection. Good enough is good enough. And making imperfect progress is certainly better than stuffing yourself at every meal.

By learning as I went along and studying for the PN Level 2 certification, I found the following practices really helped me eat more conscientiously. Here are my biggest takeaways:

- Eat slowly.
- Put your fork down between every bite.
- Eat without distractions (cell phones, computers, or TV).
- Set a timer and aim to make the meal last a minimum of ten minutes (work up to twenty or more). It takes your stomach at least twenty minutes to tell your brain that you're full. It's too easy to eat through those fullness cues if you're stuffing food in too fast.
- Eat to 80 percent full. This skill takes a long time to learn, and it can be difficult for many people (myself included). Try to think of feeling stuffed (like when your stomach aches or you feel bloated) as 100 percent full and then pare back to around 80 percent. Or, eat until you're satisfied but not stuffed. In other words, eat when you're hungry, and then instead of eating until you're full, stop eating when you're no longer hungry. There's a *huge* difference between the two.
- Check in with your body often and notice what you're feeling as you eat. (It can help to keep a journal for a little while to track this and notice any patterns.)
- Drink water. Often, we think we're hungry when we actually just need to quench our thirst.
- Learn to trust yourself.

The other incredible advantage of applying these healthier eating principles is that you'll learn to trust yourself more around food. You've probably spent a lot of time trusting other people's rules. (How has that worked out for you, by the way?) When you work toward becoming your own expert and learn to trust yourself to know what your body wants and needs, you will never again have to rely on a diet or another person to tell you how to eat. Now, this could take a lifetime to master; I'm nowhere near perfect here. But I can honestly tell you that with some practice, you will notice changes.

Trust must come with a helping of empathy and compassion. Those two ingredients will remind you, especially when you feel like you didn't eat as you intended, that you're a work in progress and worthy of acceptance just as you are. You have to practice letting go of the shame when you don't do things exactly as you intended—because those times will inevitably happen.

The wonderful thing about these tools is that they can be applied anywhere and anytime to curb overeating.

Step 2: Consume Whole Foods as Often as Possible

The majority of the meals you'll be cooking at home should consist of mostly whole foods. You know what those look like. They generally don't have labels with nutritional content listed on them. They're things your grandparents grew up eating before ultraprocessed foods became the norm. They don't usually have a long shelf life.

What's So Wrong with Processed Food?

According to Wikipedia, "Food processing is the transformation of raw ingredients into food, or of food into other forms." That frozen dinner entrée, boxed mac and cheese, or convenient taco meal in a box are examples of foods that have been overly processed and greatly altered from their natural state to extend shelf life. Other frozen items (aside from some fruits and vegetables), cookies, and many things that come from a jar can also fit this category: processed, processed, processed. One article states that 71 percent of products such as bread, salad dressings, snack foods, sweets, and sugary drinks are ultraprocessed (Northwestern University, 2019). Holy cow!

Another article written by a heart surgeon reveals that the reason processed foods are so bad for us is that those types of foods cause chronic inflammation in our bodies and can lead to heart disease, high blood pressure, diabetes, and Alzheimer's (Lundell, 2012).

ORGANIC FOODS

Deciding whether to buy organic foods is an individual choice. Some see them as too expensive, harder to find, or not worth the effort. Others eat only organic for a variety of reasons. No definitive answer exists.

However, we've established that eating whole foods in general is a better bet than overdoing ultraprocessed foods. So, it's now up to you to determine if your whole foods will also be organic. Do some research to determine if buying organic will work for you. For me, I try my hardest to buy produce in organic form if it has skin I'm going to eat (or thinner skin), and I tend to stick to the dirty dozen recommendations. But that doesn't mean I won't buy something that's not organic if it's all I can find.

DIRTY DOZEN FOOD LIST

As of 2019, the nonprofit Environmental Working Group has deemed the following as having the highest amount of pesticides when grown conventionally versus organically:

1. Strawberries
2. Spinach
3. Kale
4. Nectarines
5. Apples
6. Grapes
7. Peaches
8. Cherries
9. Pears
10. Tomatoes
11. Celery
12. Potatoes

(Bell peppers also used to be on this list consistently.)

So let's try to cut more of them out of our diets.

And here's an interesting note: a UCLA study found that cooking at home with convenience foods, such as already-packaged meals, saved just ten to twelve minutes of cooking time and that home-cooked meals averaged only thirty-four minutes to make (Sullivan, 2007). So, no more excuses for relying on those items.

Now don't think any of this is super strict. The food police aren't going to show up at your house and start throwing away your stuff. Occasionally, I buy things like tortilla shells in a bag (though I look for a healthier version made with whole wheat and fewer ingredients), packaged rye bread, or bulk sausage for a recipe. I'm just recommending you cut out the highly processed foods you are eating on a regular basis and switch them out with better choices. Just cutting back on 80–90 percent of those foods will make a huge difference. The key is to put together meals from scratch with higher-quality ingredients. I'm not asking you to quit making food you love—just to make it better.

Finding Whole Food Sources of Protein, Fats, and Carbohydrates

If you're not sure if a food is mostly a protein, carb, or fat, check out this handy website where you can find the main nutrients in foods: nutritiondata.self.com. You can search by food name, and you can also search for specific foods by type of nutrient. So if you want to cook something for dinner that's high in protein, you can go to the "Foods by Nutrient" tool and find foods that are good protein sources.

Protein: Skinless, boneless chicken breasts, salmon or other fish, shrimp, lean beef (like filet or lower-fat ground beef), eggs. Don't forget about vegetarian sources of protein: edamame with no preservatives added (also a good green veggie), quinoa (high in protein as well as being a super whole grain), beans, nuts, and cottage cheese. Even a quarter of a cup of walnuts has about seven grams of protein.

Fats: Extra virgin olive oil, grapeseed oil, walnut oil, avocados, nuts, dark chocolate, real cheese (not the stuff that comes in a bag with lots of ingredients), fatty fish (salmon, sardines, trout).

Carbs: Veggies, fruits, quinoa, farro, beans, whole wheat couscous, barley, and other whole grains.

Herbs and Spices: These add a ton of flavor, can be full of vitamins and minerals, and add only negligible calories to food.

Vegetables Are the Bomb

Veggies deserve their own heading because they are one of the most important food groups to add to your daily meals. You don't need me to go into the "why" because you already know how vital they are. And while variety may be the spice of life, consistency is the meaty part. Eating lots of different vegetables will ensure you get a host of different nutrients, but being consistent in eating them often is most important.

Play around with cooking vegetables (and check out my YouTube channel, "Lisa Schreiber," for ideas and simple veggie recipes). Try different cooking methods. Experiment with veggies you haven't tried before or those you thought you hated in the past. I'll suggest some easy ways to cook vegetables later.

Fruit

People are sometimes concerned that eating fruit can cause weight gain because of its sugar content, but don't be scared to add some every day. Fruits are loaded with fiber, which means they're processed differently in the body than straight-up added sugars. And fruits can also be a great way to get your sweet fix in without eating ultraprocessed foods. But know that they do have higher sugar contents and calories than veggies. Eating twelve bananas a day could certainly cause weight gain, so don't swap them for veggies. Rather, add them in moderation. And remember, there's a big difference between eating an apple and drinking apple juice. You lose a lot of the fiber once you start processing fruit, and fiber is one of its biggest benefits.

Feel free to go crazy with veggies, as long as you're not overdoing fats. But with fruits, consider portion sizes.

Step 3: Add, Don't Subtract

The first thing I tell people who ask how to eat in a healthier manner is to *add*, not subtract. That means adding vegetables, lean protein, healthy fats, and whole grain carbs; it's not so much about taking things away from how you currently eat. For example, do add a veggie or two every day, do add lean protein at several meals, and don't just stop eating pasta.

I have found that this additive way of thinking leaves you feeling empowered instead of deprived. And in theory, adding more nutrient-dense options leaves you feeling satiated so that you don't even want to reach for anything else. You can even try to think of healthier eating as a fun challenge. Instead of grabbing a sandwich for lunch, challenge yourself to come up with an option that includes more protein, vegetables, good fats (like olive oil or avocados), and an optional unrefined carb. Half the fun really is in knowing that you came up with a better alternative to feed your body and mind.

Start by focusing on adding real foods with as little processing as possible to your daily eating habits. Here's a guide to help you keep it simple:

Step 1: Add vegetables.

Step 2: Add protein.

Step 3: Add healthy fat.

I'm starting with vegetables because they are the most vital addition. Vegetables are carbs, but they are nutritional powerhouses because they're mostly complex carbs with no added sugars. They're also loaded with fiber and usually have very few calories. So you can eat more of them—as long as you don't go crazy with extra calories from fat sources like butter, oil, or bacon.

I mention lean protein sources on page 9, and don't forget about vegetarian sources of protein too.

Fat is generally not difficult to get in your diet, but adding healthier fats can take a little more work. You need a balance of all three types of fat (monounsaturated, polyunsaturated, and saturated), but since saturated fat is common, you should naturally get enough without trying. It's the monounsaturated and polyunsaturated fats you must focus on adding. But don't overthink it. Cook veggies in extra virgin olive oil instead of vegetable oil. Eat more foods that are naturally higher in omega-3 fatty acids like salmon, avocados, and nuts. Omega-3s help reduce inflammation in the body.

Note: Ultraprocessed products tend to contain more saturated fats, so keep an eye out for those.

Portions

I'm not telling you about portion sizes so you can worry about counting everything you eat. I'm hopeful that you'll continue to practice mindful eating techniques instead. Rather, I offer portion sizes so you can see that it doesn't take much to add protein and vegetables to your meals each day. For example, if you eat half a cup of mushrooms, half a cup of tomatoes, half a cup of carrots, and one cup of spinach, that's four vegetable servings in just one meal.

Precision Nutrition has a "handy" recommendation for portion sizes:

A serving of protein = 1 palm

A serving of vegetables = 1/2 cup for most veggies (or 1 fist) or 1 cup (2 fists) for leafy greens

A serving of carbs = 1 cupped hand

A serving of fats = 1 thumb

If you think about it, the size of your hand dictates your portion size because it's an indication of your body size. So if you have smaller hands, your recommended portion sizes will be smaller than those of someone with larger hands. That's because you need less food overall than they do.

I'm not going to tell you exact portion sizes to eat at each meal, but here are two recommendations from PN and USDA:

1. www.precisionnutrition.com/calorie-control-guide-infographic
2. snaped.fns.usda.gov/nutrition-education/nutrition-education-materials/healthy-eating-using-myplate

But again, portion sizes can be tricky, and I don't want you to get too wrapped up in them. They can depend on many factors, including your goals (weight loss or gain, weight maintenance, overall healthier eating, physical training, etc.). Because I'm advocating a lifetime of healthier eating habits, I'm focusing on moderate portion sizes, PN plate recommendations, and USDA plate recommendations.

Choose Whole Grains Rather Than Processed Grains

Keeping the wheat germ intact is what's so important about whole grain products. And though "enriched" sounds promising, its nutritional value is weakened because the whole wheat germ has been removed. Whole grains are also a better source of fiber and contain more important nutrients than other types of grains. In small amounts, white flours are probably fine. The problem is, they're found too often in food, which means you're missing out on the benefits from 100 percent whole grains. And they're taking up valuable space in your stomach when you could have made a better choice.

While you're adding (instead of subtracting) foods, try also substituting whole grains like whole wheat bread, quinoa, barley, farro, brown rice, whole wheat pasta, and oats for white or enriched products at a few meals each week. Even popcorn is a whole grain (as long as it's real popcorn and not packaged along with lots of preservatives).

EATING ON A CONTINUUM

I don't want to vilify any food, because I think this can cause binging behavior, and I also think life is too short to take the joy out of eating some of our favorite things. Instead, get in the habit of thinking about the foods you're eating on a continuum of offering "very little nutrition," "more nutrition," and "lots of nutrition." This new paradigm might make it easier to load up on foods that offer "more" and "lots of nutrition" and eat those with "very little nutrition" in moderation.

The goal is to eventually choose refined grains like white flour/white bread, white rice, and breakfast cereals sparingly.

Step 4: Read Labels

We all rely on packaged products now and then, but when you step foot in the grocery store, the overwhelming possibilities can lead to less-than-optimal choices. And that's what food companies are banking on. To keep from becoming their victim, become a savvier shopper by learning how to read labels.

Important Aspects of Reading a Label

Serving Size

Serving size tells you how much is in one serving, and servings per container indicates how many servings are in the whole package. Be mindful of how many servings you are consuming at one time. Some packages look like individual servings, but often they're not.

Calories per Serving

How many calories are in one serving? Don't let that number fool you, as it's often easy to eat more than one serving.

Total Fat

A label generally gives you information on total fat, saturated fat, and trans fat. A higher fat content is not necessarily bad, but in general, the lower the saturated fat and higher the polyunsaturated and monounsaturated fats, the better. And watch out for trans fat–free claims. The government allows food producers to claim something has no trans fats if a serving size has less than 0.49 grams. But what if you were to eat four serving sizes of a product? You may have eaten almost 2 grams of trans fats without even knowing it. So be sure to read the ingredient list. If the list includes hydrogenated or partially hydrogenated *anything*, they're hiding trans fats. Skip 'em.

WHOLE GRAINS

Here's a cool trick to check if a whole grain is actually a whole grain. Aside from checking to see if the first ingredient of a product is 100 percent whole wheat, divide the grams of carbs by ten. For every ten grams of carbs on the label, one or more grams should be fiber. So, for example, if the bread you're debating buying has twenty grams of carbs, look for at least two grams or more of fiber. This is the carbs-to-fiber 10:1 ratio, and it means that the product you're looking at is considered a whole grain.

Sodium

The American Heart Association recommends no more than 2,300 milligrams of sodium a day and is moving closer to recommending 1,500. And they also say that over 70 percent of our consumed sodium comes from packaged products, not the salt shaker. So eating whole foods more often is a great way to reduce sodium intake.

Total Carbs

Carbs are broken down on the label into fiber and sugars (and sometimes the label will include added sugars). An important measure of the quality of a carb is the amount of fiber in the product. The higher the fiber and lower the sugar count, the better, especially the added sugars. Foods like fruit and milk have natural sugars, so it's really the *added* sugar you should be more concerned with. If a label doesn't include "added sugars," take a look at the ingredient list and see how high up sugar is listed (more on that below).

Protein

Eating protein can fill you up faster and keep you fuller longer, so higher protein counts are a good thing. Because it is often difficult to find quality protein in packaged goods, it's important to get more protein from whole food sources, rather than rely on packaged products. You're likely to see only a modicum of protein in a processed product, followed by a high amount of carbs and added sugars.

Ingredient List

The order of ingredients is important because they are listed by weight. So the higher up the ingredient, the more of it in the product. Be sure the first few ingredients are quality ones, like 100 percent whole wheat or tomatoes, or that they contain the main product (like pickles) followed by simple ingredients like water.

As Michael Pollan says in his book *In Defense of Food: An Eater's Manifesto*, if a product contains items your great-grandmother wouldn't recognize, skip it and find something better. Look for items with shorter ingredient lists. If that package of bread you're looking at has twenty ingredients, you can bet it's not the best option. Replace it with one that has just a few ingredients, and preferably ones you can pronounce. Try the store's bakery for breads with fewer ingredients.

If sugar, or some form of it, is one of the top three

ingredients, or if an item has more than five grams of added sugar, it's best to minimize consumption of it. And remember, added sugar is sugar. Whether it's in the form of agave, pure cane sugar, honey, high-fructose corn syrup, dextrose, or beet sugar, it's still added sugar. Take a look at the ingredient list to see whether sugars are naturally occurring or if they've been added.

I have no idea what "natural flavors" means, and food manufacturers aren't required to tell you. But they are likely highly processed and contain chemicals. Remember, moderation is important.

Other Packaging Info

Be careful of labels on packaged foods that tout things like "natural," "healthy," "low-fat," "low-carb," or "low-calorie." They're usually buzzwords created by food manufacturers to reel you in. They don't mean much, as they're usually signs that ingredients have been replaced with something else (like sugar or artificial products). Read the list of ingredients instead. Do you sense a theme here?

APPS

Take advantage of smartphone apps, such as Fooducate, that allow you to scan grocery store items to see a rating based on nutritional content.

Step 5: Balance Your Meals

I was recently laid up for over a month after spraining both my wrists in a cycling accident (something I do not recommend). For at least two weeks, I couldn't cook anything because the pain kept me from putting any pressure on either wrist. We relied on meal-delivery services to get us through this tough period, and it was a major, in-your-face reminder that most of the food you get when you eat out is loaded with processed carbs, saturated fats, and less-than-ideal protein. The option to order balanced meals was virtually nonexistent. Yes, anomalies are out there, offering healthier options, but sadly, they are few and far between. What a relief when I was able to start cooking again.

This experience was a reminder that it is up to each of us to make the best choices. No factory or restaurant is going to help us do it.

Cooking shows and magazines rarely offer ideas for balanced meals—only single dishes. So putting a meal together is something you'll have to figure out on your own, which can seem like assembling an Ikea bookshelf or completing a four-thousand-piece jigsaw puzzle.

But balancing a meal isn't super complicated once you know its parts: protein, vegetables and fruits, healthy fat, and an optional (preferably whole) grain. At a minimum, a balanced meal should have some protein, at least one vegetable serving, and a healthy fat source.

The confusion comes because it's rare that you'll eat a plain piece of chicken or meat without any kind of flavor to enhance it, or a vegetable that hasn't been cooked in oil or butter. How do you count everything? In the hopes of making your healthy-eating lifestyle easier, I'd prefer you to think about the ingredients you're using instead of ob-sessing over every little detail of what's on your plate.

Exactly what should you be eating? That's entirely up to you. And I hate the word "should" because it suggests there is one right way to do things. Dieting is a waste of time and doesn't stick long term; many studies—as well as firsthand experience—confirm this. But if you're seeking better overall nutrition, balanced meals are an important factor because they give your body a greater chance of getting a variety of necessary nutrients. Filling your plate first with veggies, fruits, lean proteins, healthier fats, and whole grain carbs (with fewer processed carbs) is key.

In order to balance your meals, ask yourself this question each time you sit down to eat: can I add at least one vegetable and/or some lean protein to this meal? The answer may be no, but the habit of asking this question leads to having balanced meals more often, which means you'll get a wider variety of nutrients each day.

You can even make a snack more balanced. For example, instead of eating an apple by itself, add some peanut butter for healthy fat and protein. (Be sure to check the ingredient list on the peanut butter and stay away from jars with a high sugar content.) Or, you can dip carrots and celery into hummus for veggies, fat, and protein. It may seem like you're eating more food, but doing this will keep your blood sugar balanced and make you feel fuller longer.

Not all your meals will be "perfect." In fact, many of them won't come close. You'd probably feel absurd asking your friend to roast some brussels sprouts when you're visiting for dinner because she didn't think to make a vegetable; you don't want to be *that* person. It's okay to have meals that are "off." As you become more aware of what you are taking in, you improve your chances of getting key nutrients from food every day.

There's no one right way to make a balanced plate, but veggies, lean protein, and healthy fat are always required. Here are a few examples of my balanced meals:

Balsamic-Roasted Salmon (protein),
Shallot-and-Garlic-Sautéed Edamame (veggie, healthy fat)

Garlic-and-Herb-Goat-Cheese-Stuffed Chicken Breasts
(protein, healthy fat), Cauliflower Rice (veggie, healthy
fat), Spicy Sautéed Mushrooms (veggie, healthy fat)

*Cilantro-Lime
Chicken with
Avocado Salsa
(protein, veggies,
and healthy fat),
Kale Salad (veggie)*

*Baked Salmon (protein), Broccolini
(vegetable, healthy fat), Quinoa (whole grain carb)*

*Spinach Salad with Cherry Tomatoes, Grilled Shrimp,
Homemade Vinaigrette (veggie, protein, healthy fat)*

*Balsamic Chicken (protein),
Cauliflower Pancakes (veggie, healthy fat)*

I've already talked about the concept of adding and not subtracting, especially in the beginning. This definitely applies to balanced meals. If you find yourself eating pasta every night, start by adding some vegetables and lean protein and working on building a more balanced plate.

Remember, this is not an all-or-nothing lifestyle. I think of myself as an 80–90 percenter, which means I eat healthier meals 80–90 percent of the time, and then I don't focus on it too much the other 10–20 percent. What's your goal? Be sure to remember your why!

Okay, I'm done with the healthier eating lecture. Whew. That wasn't so bad, was it?

Habit-Based Exercise for Establishing Healthier Habits

Begin when you're ready, withhold judgment, and start over as many times as you need to.

Week 1: Be mindful at one meal every day. This means you pay attention to how your body feels when you're eating. Putting your fork down after every bite and timing your meal can also make you more aware.

Week 2: Be mindful at two meals every day.

Week 3 and beyond: Be mindful at every meal.

Week 4: Add one veggie every day.

Week 5: Add two to three veggies a day and see if you can work up to four or five fruits and veggies a day.

Week 6: Add a lean protein serving at one meal per day.

Week 7: Add a lean protein serving at two to three meals per day.

Week 8: Cook with healthier fats, like extra virgin olive oil, at one meal a day.

Week 9: Work up to cooking with healthier fats at three meals a day.

Week 10: Replace one processed carb each week with a whole grain.

Week 11: Work up to replacing processed carbs with a whole grain four to five times a week.

Week 12: Try to balance one meal a day.

Week 13: Try to balance two meals each day.

Week 14: Work up to balancing three meals each day.

Checklist for
Establishing Healthier Habits

Below is a table you can use (or go to lisakschreiber.com/the-meal-deal-book) to help you keep track of these habits. Put a checkmark for each time you were successful with your new habit. And do *not* beat yourself up if it takes time to make these habits come to life. Every meal is a new beginning.

And remember, none of these habits happened for me overnight, or even very quickly. It took years of consistency for them to stick. I'm hoping this book will speed that process up for you.

Add a checkmark for each time you successfully complete the action. Add an X for when you don't. *No judgment*. It's just a mark.

		S	M	T	W	T	F	S
Week 1	Be mindful at one meal. Try tips from Step 1: Eat Mindfully.							
Week 2	Be mindful at two meals. Try practice tips.							
Week 3	Be mindful at every meal. Try practice tips.							
Week 4	Add one veggie every day.							
Week 5	Add two to three veggies every day.							
Week 6	Add lean protein at one meal per day.							
Week 7	Add lean protein at two to three meals per day.							
Week 8	Cook with healthier fats, like extra virgin olive oil, at one meal a day.							
Week 9	Work up to cooking with healthier fats at three meals a day.							

	S	M	T	W	T	F	S
Week 10 Replace one processed carb with whole grain this week.							
Week 11 Replace processed carb with whole grain four to five times per week.							
Week 12 Try to balance one meal a day.							
Week 13 Try to balance two meals a day.							
Week 14 Try to balance three meals a day.							

As I said, my ultimate goal for you is to practice healthier eating habits, like mindful eating and cooking at home with whole foods, more often. However, if, for whatever reason, dieting is your jam, the fundamentals I'm introducing here can be used to enhance your diet goals. It's nearly impossible to diet well if you don't set up your environment and practice new eating habits.

Once you make it a habit to bring mindfulness into most of your eating situations, all the other meal-planning techniques become second nature because you'll have the skills to be in control of any food encounter.

You will have established fundamentals you can always rely on.

But using other meal-planning tools will also help you control your home environment and make your habits even easier to stick with. So let's do a kitchen makeover to set up your surroundings to fit your new food lifestyle.

Chapter 2

PERFORM A KITCHEN MAKEOVER

Everyone knows the kitchen is a place where our meals are prepped, cooked, and served. However, there are some of us who consider it as a classroom for learning some of life's most insightful and thought-provoking lessons.
—Johnny Tan, *From My Mama's Kitchen*

I consider myself a fairly disciplined person in that I don't feel a particular call to finish an entire bag of chocolate in one sitting. But I'm also human. I once found myself eating chocolate every night, whether out of boredom or just not paying attention. When I realized this was happening more than I was comfortable with, I had to give my pantry a once-over and decide whether this chocolate needed to go or whether I could consume it in moderation.

The first few times I helped others perform a kitchen makeover, it became very clear that not a lot of thought goes into the foods we buy. But it's imperative to think about it because what's right in front of us is what we will eat most often. So setting up our environment to complement our new eating habits is essential.

In this chapter, I'll help you decide what foods you want to keep based on the new eating guidelines you establish, and I'll help you set up your environment to reflect those guidelines. Your pantry will be organized, you'll know where to find everything when you're cooking, and, most important, you'll be on your way to having more nutritious food choices within reach. All these improvements will help you be more consistent with your long-term healthy-eating goals.

Red-Light, Yellow-Light, Green-Light Kitchen Makeover Method

In keeping with the Precision Nutrition "Traffic Light" system, we're going to use the red-light, yellow-light, green-light method to take inventory of what's currently in your kitchen. We'll put items into three piles and then, based on parameters you set, decide what's staying and what's being tossed (or donated).

Before beginning the action steps below, write out a list of parameters you'd like to follow. Here are a few questions to get you started:

- Do you want to keep only items that have less than five grams of sugar?
- Do you want to get rid of anything that is ultraprocessed or has fifteen or more ingredients (many of which you can't pronounce)?
- Are you going to keep the foods that tempt you to binge?
- Do you want to swap some of the processed grains for whole grains?

- Do you want to throw out everything that has trans fats?

Use chapter 1 as your healthier eating framework, but these parameters are entirely up to you depending on your goals.

Now, let's take that list and start making piles.

Red-Light Items

Foods that are ultraprocessed, have trans fats, are high in sugar, or are easy to binge on belong in this pile. These foods are only bad for you. Maybe you can't stop eating them or they make you feel bad or you can't tolerate them.

Yellow-Light Items

Yellow-light foods are foods you're on the fence about for one reason or another and need to address again later. Maybe you can eat a little bit of them and not binge on them.

Green-Light Items

Green-light foods are those you feel confident will enhance your eating habits: fresh veggies and fruits, lean protein, beans, healthier cooking oils, whole grains, spices, and condiments with few ingredients. You feel good when you eat them, so they're always a yes.

Red-Light, Yellow-Light, Green-Light: Go

1. Designate three categories on your counter. You can label the areas with a sheet of paper or piece of tape.
2. Pull one item out of your pantry at a time. To avoid overwhelm, you can do this one shelf at a time. It's fine if it takes days or weeks to do this.
3. Toss anything beyond its expiration date. (If you still need that item, write it on your grocery list.)
4. Read each label, keeping your parameters in mind.
5. Decide which pile the item belongs in (red, yellow, or green).
6. Trash or donate the red-light foods to someone in need. (Unfortunately, way too many people could use those items to survive.)
7. Put the green-light items back in the pantry. (I'll talk about organizing them in the next chapter, but start by grouping similar items together.)
8. Review the yellow-light items again. For example, you might think about white flour products, items with trans fats, or sweets that scream "eat me" in one sitting. Keep the bag of chocolate chips if you're going to bake with them. If you're completely unsure of what to do with these items, put them back in the pantry and revisit them at a later date.

Hint: If a food screams "eat me," it's important to consider getting rid of it so you'd have to go out to get it.

Voilà! Your pantry is already looking more organized, and you are beginning to feel more in control.

Repeat steps for items in your refrigerator and freezer (like condiments, frozen foods, etc.).

My Red-Light, Yellow-Light, and Green-Light Items

Red Light

While I've eliminated most red-light items by now, here are examples of things I've had in the past: anything with trans fats or boxed items that have ingredients I can barely pronounce, Crisco, crackers with hydrogenated oil, bagged popcorn with artificial flavors (I keep fresh popcorn now and make it from scratch), boxed stuffing mixes.

Yellow Light

These items are harder to define. An example of a yellow-light item for me is a bag of fun-size Baby Ruth candy bars, which is really only a problem for me at Halloween. If I can eat just one every few days and be satisfied, I'll keep them around. If I know I will eat the entire bag at one time, it probably needs to go. Or if I'm actively trying to lose weight, I keep them out of the house so I'm not tempted to overeat.

Green Light

I always keep whole grains like quinoa and whole wheat couscous on hand for a fast, nutritious carb. Whole fruits like bananas, oranges, and apples are a great choice for snacks. Nuts also make an easy snack. Cooking ingredients

COMPROMISE

My husband's red-light foods are not generally the same as mine. If you share food with someone else and their foods are a trigger for you, work together to decide what to keep. You might negotiate to buy certain foods only some of the time or agree to go out to get them instead of keeping them around. Another workable compromise is to store foods in an opaque container, thus keeping them hidden from the triggered person's view. Even putting them on a high shelf or just out of sight could be helpful. Consider buying single servings of snacks like potato chips so you're not mindlessly eating them, or buy treats your significant other or child likes but you don't.

like olive oil, vinegars, and spices are a must in your green-light category because they complement your new cooking-at-home adventure.

Warning

Many of us have an emotional attachment to certain foods in our pantries. For me, that includes chocolate. For my husband, it's potato chips. If you find you're hesitant to ditch something, or just not sure you're ready to do without it yet, it is imperative that you *go easy on yourself.* Judgment and self-criticism should not be part of this process, because self-condemning thoughts can lead to shame and, ultimately, binging.

You can always revisit problematic items later. There's no point in making yourself feel bad over food. It doesn't lead to anything productive. The most important thing is that you're adding more nutritious items. Doing that alone can lead to healthier habits down the line.

To see this concept in action, check out a video on my YouTube channel called "Kitchen Makeover with Jenifer" that I made with my best friend.

Habit-Based Exercise for Making Over Your Kitchen

Moving forward, when you go to the grocery store each week, shop within your new parameters and stick to bringing home green-light foods. Then, you won't have to do a kitchen makeover again (or at least not for a long time) or worry you're going to binge. Buying healthy choices means you'll consistently have a pantry stocked with better-quality foods.

Checklist for Making Over Your Kitchen

Add a checkmark for each time you successfully complete the action. Add an X for when you don't. *No judgment*. It's just a mark.

Week	1	2	3	4	5	6	7
Use your parameters to buy mostly green-light foods.							

Once you've set up your environment so that it becomes easier to reach for more minimally processed foods, you'll be establishing the habit of eating those foods instead of high-sugar and ultraprocessed packaged goods because, in general, what's closest is what you go for. It will require effort to go out and buy processed items if they're not reliably in arm's reach.

Now let's take advantage of that kitchen makeover by gradually restocking items and organizing them so that you're prepared to cook with ease and efficiency.

Chapter 3

STOCK YOUR KITCHEN WELL

*Get people back into the kitchen and combat
the trend toward processed food and fast food.*
—Andrew Weil

Several years ago during a freak ice storm in Atlanta (of which we generally have very few), I almost got nervous because I had just gotten home from out of town and didn't have time to go to the grocery store to stock up before the storm hit. I had bought a few essentials before I left, but didn't know if I had enough to keep us afloat for what could be a few days. When it snows in Atlanta, the entire city shuts down. I thought I'd better take a look through the pantry and freezer to make sure we had enough food to survive without an emergency grocery store trip (where I was sure to be greeted by hundreds of harried customers). And, thank goodness, we did. The roads were completely iced over, but we were fortunate we didn't have to leave the house for what turned out to be almost a week.

My husband will attest to the fact that I am not a well-organized person in most respects. No one would accuse me of being Martha Stewart unless they're being *way* nice. But, I've found that organization is the key to having a well-stocked kitchen and space to move around freely while cooking. And I know what you're thinking: how can this disorganized mess of a person be giving me advice on being organized? Well, I think that being a disorganized mess gives me credibility because, despite my disorganized ways, my kitchen is always a well-oiled machine. And if I can achieve this, you most certainly can too.

Part of the reason my kitchen is in good order is because my husband is extremely well organized and has figured out the best way to have the kitchen set up for my needs. It's also because, over the years, I have managed to keep it this way. I like knowing where all my utensils are, that they're within easy reach, and that I won't have to wade through a messy drawer to find what I need. It keeps me from burning the garlic while searching for the right spatula. I also like knowing my spices are properly stored in the pantry. All of this makes me more efficient. When we recently moved after thirteen years in the same house, I was instrumental in organizing my new gourmet kitchen. With as much practice as I've had, I'd venture to say that if I had to organize a kitchen completely by myself in the future, I could do so.

Let's Get Stockin'

Keeping essential items in your kitchen at all times will ensure that you never have to make a last-minute run to the store for missing items. It also makes it a lot easier to prepare a backup meal if your first attempt at a recipe fails. I'll suggest items you should consider keeping on hand,

and you will discover many of your own, based on your taste preferences, as you go along. I'll also discuss important cooking utensils to keep in the kitchen as well as good storage methods. This will allow you to move through your kitchen like a dancer in a well-choreographed show.

Setting up your kitchen in advance allows you to start with a clean slate, and restocking allows you to get right to work planning your meals without the added stress of finding a place for any new items or looking through a stuffed pantry.

By the end of this chapter, you should have everything you need to make complete meals and know exactly where in your kitchen to find it. Let's start by adding in the ingredients that will keep your healthier kitchen well stocked.

Items may vary depending on your personal tastes. For example, maybe you cook Italian, Japanese, or Indian food often and need to keep certain spices on hand. Maybe you don't like quinoa but love whole wheat couscous. Perhaps you like black olives but hate the green ones. I'm going to share my must-haves, but you can adjust the list according to your tastes.

Pantry Staples

Olive oil
Canola oil
Sesame oil
Salt (I prefer course kosher)
Pepper (I use a pepper mill with freshly ground black pepper, so I always keep a backup of fresh black peppercorns in the pantry)

White sugar
Brown sugar
All-purpose flour
Whole wheat flour
Chicken broth/stock
Canned tomatoes (usually a fourteen-ounce can of diced tomatoes will suffice)
Canned black olives
Tomato sauce
Tomato paste
Canned chipotles in adobo
Salsa
Soy sauce
Worcestershire sauce
White vinegar
Cider vinegar
Balsamic vinegar
Rice wine vinegar
Garlic powder
Onion powder
Panko/bread crumbs
Dried spices you use frequently (oregano, basil, thyme, cumin, paprika, red pepper flakes, cayenne pepper, etc.)
Homemade spice mix(es) (see link to my favorite recipe in chapter 9)
Pastas
Fresh garlic
Onions
Rice (your choice) and/or couscous
Quinoa
Evaporated milk

Refrigerator Staples

Lemon juice
Greek yogurt
Parmesan cheese
Hot sauce
Sriracha
Lemons
Limes
Chili paste
Mayonnaise
Mustards

Essential Non-Food Items

Aluminum foil
Nonstick foil
Plastic wrap
Ziplock bags (large and small)
Parchment paper
Paper bags (these come in handy for ripening avocados)
Two cutting boards: one for raw meat, poultry, and seafood (preferably nonporous material like plastic so you can put in the dish washer); one for everything else, like fresh produce and breads (preferably a good wooden board)

Essential Tools and Utensils

My feeling is that the simplest tools are the most effective in the kitchen. You probably don't need all the special gadgets, which take up precious countertop and cabinet space and serve very little purpose. You know the ones I'm talking about: the corn cob peeler, the garlic crusher. In theory, these items seem like great fun. But knowing how to properly use a knife will come in handy.

That being said, here are some utensils I think are indispensable:

Liquid measuring cups
Dry measuring cups
Measuring spoons
Microplane/grater
Handheld grater
Spatulas (I prefer non-metal so I don't ruin my nonstick cookware)
Wooden spoons
Variety of mixing bowls
Basting/pastry brush
Whisks (I like to keep three on hand: one large metal, one small metal, and one medium-to-large silicone whisk for use with nonstick pots and pans)
Blender
Hand and/or stand mixer
Colander
Digital thermometer
Soup ladle
Spider or other small sieve with a handle
Tongs
Vegetable peeler
Can opener
Skewers
Oil mister (I've been using this for years and absolutely *love* it. I bought one recommended by America's Test Kitchen, after reading about how many cooking sprays contain glues and other icky, non-food-related items. With the oil mister, I just use regular olive oil,

which I always have on hand. This saves money over buying those spray cans. Plus, who wants to eat glue besides a five-year-old?)

Small mandolin (I use this to quickly slice things like potatoes if I have a lot of them)

Oven mitts

Trivets

Food processor (*optional*)

Immersion blender (*optional*)

The Minimalist Kitchen

A lot of the organizing will fall into place when you start cooking more and realize the things you prefer to use.

Important Pots and Pans

10-inch nonstick skillet

10-inch stainless-steel skillet (with lid)

Steamer (with lid)

1 1/2 qt. pot (with lid)

3 qt. pot (with lid)

4 qt. pot (with lid)

Roasting pan

Several baking sheets/jelly roll pans that have a lip so food doesn't drop off the edge (essential for roasting vegetables, especially now that you're going to be making more of them)

9 x 13-inch glass or metal baking pan

Meatloaf pan or square baking pan

Knives

Speaking of some of the most important tools to have in your kitchen, investing in decent knives is almost nonnegotiable. They are a cook's best friend—like an extra appendage. They don't have to be expensive, and you only need a few quality ones. And *never*, I repeat, *never* put good knives into the dishwasher. It will ruin them. Also, *never* put a knife into a sink of soapy water unless you're going to wash it immediately. I learned that one the hard way (as have many before me) with a massive slice to the hand. It can also damage the knife to leave it drowning in water.

Important Knives to Have

Chef's knife and/or 7-inch Santoku
Paring knife
Serrated-edge knife for slicing bread and some other
   items (like tomatoes)
Boning knife for cutting meats

Optional Knives

Smaller utility and/or 5-inch Santoku knife
Good pair of kitchen shears to cut through bones or hard
   shells

Utensil Storage Steps

Optional: Buy boxes to store utensils in drawers

Step 1: Pull out utensils and lay on counter.

Step 2: Group/sort utensils by putting similar items together in new piles.

Step 3: Put new piles in storage boxes or directly back in drawers based on frequency of use. (The more frequently used items should be closer to the cooking area.)

It may take trial and error to figure out the best organization for your kitchen based on how you cook and what utensils you use most often.

My Kitchen Setup

Counter Storage

Spatulas and wooden spoons: I keep these next to the stove in a large canister.

Knives, including kitchen shears: I prefer to keep these in a knife block on the counter for easy access, but you could also hang a wall mount and store them next to the stove. *Do not* store knives haphazardly in a drawer. That's how accidents happen.

Salt, pepper mill, olive oil, canola oil, oil mister: I keep these on the counter next to the stove because they are, by far, my most-used items.

Canisters with flour, sugar, and protein powder: I use protein powder every now and then for quick, nutritious shakes.

Single-serve/regular blender: I use these for making shakes.

Storage in Drawers
and Cabinets near Stove

Note: Some of these are things I personally use often, but I don't consider them essential because everyone cooks differently.

Measuring cups and spoons
Baking sheets (jelly roll pans)
Cutting boards
Most-used pots and pans
Strainers/colanders
Silverware
Food storage containers
Aluminum foil, nonstick foil, plastic wrap, large and
    small storage bags
Whisks
Tongs
Shrimp deveiner
Skewers
Ice cream scoop
Melon ballers
Oven mitts
Trivets

Pantry Storage

Spices: If your pantry isn't near your stove, you might want to store your most-used spices somewhere closer to the stove, like a drawer or an over-the-counter, built-in rack.

Nuts

Flours, oats, panko

Baking goods

Sugars, cornstarch

Crackers

Oils and vinegars

Soups

Quinoa, couscous, rice, and pastas

Extra condiments

Extra spices

Other Cupboards

Extra pots and pans, not used as often

Hand and stand mixer

Toaster

Small mandolin

Glasses

Dishes

Keep in Mind while Organizing

When organizing your kitchen, here are a few main

BACKUP SHOPPING

Keep your shopping list nearby so you can add items to it as you see you're running low. For example, if you take the mustard or mayonnaise out of the fridge and discover you've only got a few teaspoons left, write it on the list to pick up on your next grocery store run. Better to have extra than run to the store at the last minute, especially if you're already in the middle of cooking. I always keep a backup of those types of items in my pantry, and when I need the item, I put it in the fridge, place it on the shopping list, and buy one to keep stored in the pantry for the next time I'm running low.

concepts to consider as you set up your environment to fit your cooking style:

- Group similar items together.
- Items you use often should be easy to reach.
- Don't overcrowd items.
- Items you need to use quickly should be close to the stove.
- Put less frequently used items on higher shelves.

Habit-Based Exercise
for Stocking Your Kitchen

Week 1 (or as many weeks as you need): Add several ingredients from the well-stocked kitchen list (or ingredients you find yourself using often) to your grocery list and buy them on your next trip. Place them in their proper place on your gorgeous, newly organized shelves.

Checklist for Stocking Your Kitchen

Add a checkmark for each time you successfully complete the action. Add an X for when you don't. *No judgment*. It's just a mark.

Week	1	2	3	4	5	6	7
Add ingredients from the well-stocked kitchen list (or your own).							

Now that your kitchen is a clean slate, let's get down to business and make weekly menu plans. And that starts with the important first step of finding recipes based on your new, healthier eating guidelines. So let's take a look at where to find those precious gems.

Chapter 4

FIND RECIPES

*You don't have to cook fancy or complicated masterpieces—
just good food from fresh ingredients.*

—Julia Child

When I first started cooking more frequently, I had basically the same five-meal rotation. And those meals mostly consisted of pastas and ultraprocessed, boxed products. Then, when I decided to start cooking with more whole foods, I figured following a recipe was a great place to start because I didn't have to reinvent the wheel. I learned a tremendous amount by watching Rachael Ray, and it was refreshing because she's so laid-back and her recipes are simple with little measuring. I felt no pressure to get it perfect.

It took some time to figure out what I wanted in a recipe and then to start accumulating them, but gradually I noticed I had a stack of recipes I loved. For as long as I've been cooking and meal planning, I still use recipes as my guide most of the time. It takes the pressure off me to invent a new meal every time I cook, and I know it will turn out because I've made it many times before.

The first step to meal planning is to assemble a collection of recipes that you and your family actually like. Obviously, this is easier said than done.

When I type "chicken recipes" into Google, I get over a billion results. And that number grows every day. Even doing the same at foodnetwork.com yields over nineteen thousand results. What is a meal planner to do?

Recipes are an indispensable part of the meal-planning process. The ingredients and measurements have been tested over and over, and they work for a reason. By following recipes in the beginning, you will learn invaluable cooking techniques, which will give you the knowledge to eventually bring together ingredients on your own, if you so desire. And recipes are priceless, because if you wing it all the time, you are unlikely to have ingredients on hand to complete an entire meal. Plus, by using recipes made with whole foods, you'll know beforehand that you're using quality ingredients in your dishes.

As much as I'd like to get to know all of you, I don't know what you like. But I will give you tips on where to find recipes, what to look for, and general ideas to throw together quick meals with quality ingredients. The whole point of this book is for you to become self-sufficient in the kitchen and, eventually, your own meal-planning authority. As opposed to "diet" books, where you're more limited or more restricted, this approach can make it a fun task to choose your own recipes because you get to be in charge based on your tastes and lifestyle. After all, at some point, you have to stop following somebody else's diet.

By the end of this chapter, you'll have a strong selection of healthier recipes from which to choose nutritious, balanced meals each week. You'll no longer be at the mercy of a cooking show, cookbook, or magazine to create menus with recipes you like.

Where to Find Recipes

The problem with recipes is the endless supply of them. The internet is a magnificent tool, but unless you know how to use it efficiently, it doesn't do much good. I'd like to offer a few ideas to give you an advantage when looking through recipes. Then, you won't panic and give up from overwhelm when you type "chicken recipes" into a search engine.

The internet, television, and cookbooks you already own offer an ample amount of free recipes and are pretty much everything you need to take control of your weekly menu planning. And you probably already have dozens of cookbooks on hand. Peruse away. A subscription to a great cooking magazine, like *Cook's Illustrated* or *EatingWell*, is a welcome and fairly inexpensive addition to any kitchen.

I'll provide keys to using cookbooks, magazines, and website resources to their best advantage so you can more easily synthesize that information into weekly menu plans.

It only takes about thirty seconds to read a recipe, and many you can eliminate at first glance. By frequently looking through recipes and making new meals, you're going to grow into knowing immediately which recipes you'll like. I rarely prepare a recipe that doesn't make it to my "cookbook," because I've been searching long enough to know what to look for and how it's going to taste.

Recipe Sources

General Food Websites

www.foodnetwork.com
www.cookscountry.com*
www.americastestkitchen.com/recipes*
www.pinterest.com
cooking.nytimes.com
www.washingtonpost.com/food (I love to use their recipe finder)*
www.epicurious.com
www.cookinglight.com
www.allrecipes.com
www.myrecipes.com
www.bigoven.com

* As of this writing, these websites give you a limited number of recipes for free; it's a paid subscription after that.

Websites That Allow You to Search by Ingredient

www.bigoven.com/recipes/leftover
myfridgefood.com
www.supercook.com/#/recipes
recipeland.com/recipes/by_ingredient
www.recipepuppy.com

Cookbooks

Vegetables Every Day: The Definitive Guide to Buying and Cooking Today's Produce, with More Than 350 Recipes, by Jack Bishop

Weber's New Real Grilling: The Ultimate Cookbook for Every Backyard Griller, by Jamie Purviance

The America's Test Kitchen Family Cookbook 3rd Edition: Cookware Rating Edition, by America's Test Kitchen

Fast Food Fix: 75+ Amazing Recipe Makeovers of Your Fast Food Restaurant Favorites, by Devin Alexander

The Big Book of Soups and Stews: 262 Recipes for Serious Comfort Food, by Maryana Vollstedt

Cooking Magazines

Cook's Illustrated
Food Network Magazine
EatingWell
Saveur
Food & Wine
Gourmet
Southern Living
Every Day with Rachael Ray

Cooking Shows

America's Test Kitchen (PBS) – a favorite to learn technique
Cook's Country (PBS) – another favorite to learn technique
The Pioneer Woman (Food Network)
Barefoot Contessa (Food Network)
Valerie's Home Cooking (Food Network)
Giada at Home (Food Network)
30-Minute Meals (Food Network)

Food Newsletters

New York Times (www.nytimes.com/newsletters/cooking)
Real Simple (www.realsimple.com/magazine-more/newsletters/real-simple-daily-recipe-newsletter)

Cooking Light
(www.cookinglight.com/newsletter/index.html?iframe
url=http://ebm.cheetahmail.com/r/regf2)
MyRecipes (www.myrecipes.com/newsletters)
Taste of Home (www.tasteofhome.com/sign-up-for-free-
newsletters)
Cooking Channel
(mynewsletters.scrippsnetworks.com/?mode=subscrib
e&nlbrand=cooking)
Food & Wine (www.foodandwine.com/newsletter-sign-up)

Apps for iPhone

Prices are given as of time of writing.
Fooducate (free)
America's Test Kitchen (free)
Epicurious (free)
Pinterest (free)
Yummly (free)
Weber Grills (free)
Food Network Kitchen (free)
Food Network GO (free) – includes ten-thousand-plus
free episodes
Tasty (free)
Paprika Recipe Manager ($4.99)

Apps for Android

Food Network Kitchen (free)
Pinterest (free)
AllRecipes Dinner Spinner (free)

Is Your Recipe Worthy?

Once you know what to look for, it only takes a few seconds to read through a recipe and decide if it's something you'd like to try.

Step 1	Read ingredient list.
Step 2	Consider total time.
Step 3	Check difficulty rating.
Step 4	Scan reviews.
Step 5	Look at number of servings.
Step 6	Read directions.

Step 1: Read Ingredient List

Use suggestions from the healthier eating guidelines to choose recipes and stick to recipes that use mostly whole foods and your green-light items. (See two different versions of a recipe, one I recommend and one I don't, for an example on page 65.) If you notice too many ultraprocessed ingredients, move along. If a recipe has a shorter list of ingredients, look for bold flavors to avoid ending up with a bland meal.

Step 2: Consider Total Time

You can bet it will always take longer than they suggest, so be sure you're willing to invest the time to make it. Recipes with shorter cook times are a great way to feel comfortable in the kitchen. Also, be sure to consider hands-on time versus total cooking time. Often, it takes longer to make a meal, but the hands-on time is actually very short. If you want to eat sooner, consider a shorter overall cooking time. If there's no rush, the overall cooking time might not matter, though you might not want to spend an hour of hands-on cooking time.

Step 3: Check Difficulty Rating (if given)

The more advanced the recipe, the longer it's likely to take. Save more challenging recipes for the weekend or nights when you have more time. The last thing you want is to spend an hour cooking the meal and then clean for another hour because you used ten pots and pans.

Step 4: Scan Reviews

See if the recipe has been rated by others. I generally stick to four- and five-star recipes, especially if they have been tried by many users. Reviews are a great point of reference because they've been made by everyday home cooks who will gladly tell you what they liked and didn't like about the recipe. You don't have to read through all the reviews (or any of them, really), but the more ratings a recipe has, the more you can probably rely on the reviews.

Step 5: Look at Number of Servings

Make sure there's enough to feed the number of people you have for dinner. If you want leftovers, consider doubling a recipe.

Step 6: Read Directions

If you've decided to try the recipe, quickly read through the directions to make sure it doesn't seem too challenging and that there isn't something that would keep you from making it (for example, a long marinating time or twenty steps).

How to Search for Recipes

Step 1   Pull up your favorite food websites.
Step 2   Perform a general search by using terms like "chicken," "beef," "vegetables," "casseroles," etc.
Step 3   Narrow your search.
Step 4   Scroll and click on enticing recipes.
Step 5   Save recipe to try it.

Step 1: Pull Up Your Favorite Food Websites (or Use Some of My Favorites)

For example, go to **foodnetwork.com** and find the search tool, which usually looks like a magnifying glass.

Step 2: Perform a General Search by Using Terms like "Chicken," "Beef," "Pasta," "Vegetables," "Casseroles," Etc.

As you read the recipe names, decide what sounds appealing at the moment. You'll be surprised when you start doing this that a certain type of recipe will call to you.

Step 3: Narrow Your Search

You'll get a whole lot of recipes at these websites, but don't panic. This is just a jumping-off point.

There are two ways to go about this. First, if you know what flavor you're in the mood for, you could type that into the search window. For example, pick a protein plus a flavor:

Protein/Main Dish	Flavor Profile
Chicken	Teriyaki
Beef	BBQ
Pork	Garlic
Lamb	Curry
Fish	Cilantro
Pasta	Lemon
Vegetable	Soy Sauce
Eggs	Honey Mustard

In chapter 10 I provide a list of flavor types to narrow down ingredients depending on what type of flavor you're looking to replicate.

Second, you could do a broad search and narrow it down. Scroll down the list of recipes and become inspired by the suggestions.

After being inspired, go back to the search tool and enter the specific search term that caught your eye. For example, you could type in "chicken parmesan" and start looking closely at those recipes. This is likely to lead you to other ideas as well.

You can also take some of your favorite ingredients and do a Google search combining them. For example, I love cilantro, so I might look up "cilantro + chicken." My husband really likes teriyaki, so I might search for "teriyaki + hamburgers." The idea is to narrow down your search before you hit the almighty Google or other search engine and become overwhelmed with the choices.

I've given just a few ideas. You'll be able to refine your search even further once you get started.

Step 4: Scroll and Click on Enticing Recipes

Eliminate any recipes with ingredients in the title that you don't like or any that have low ratings. If there are pictures, does the dish look like something you'd love to make?

Remember, choosing recipes that contain mostly whole foods and fit into your green-light guidelines is crucial.

Step 5: Save Recipe to Try It

You have several options for saving a recipe. You can print the recipe and put it in your binder of recipes to try. I'll discuss this more in chapter 5.

Or, you can save recipes to Pinterest by creating a board of "Recipes to Try," or you can create separate folders labeled "Chicken Recipes to Try," "Beef Recipes to Try," "Breakfast Recipes to Try," "Soup Recipes to Try," etc.

Emailing recipes to yourself is another option. Or, create a document in your favorite word processor (I use

RECIPE COLLECTION TIPS

If you choose to save the recipe online, you risk the possibility of it being taken down from the website. So if you really want to make it, I suggest printing it out or saving it in a Word document.

If you don't store these recipes somewhere you can see them, you'll very likely forget about them or not know where to find them when you want to make them again.

Microsoft Word) and copy and paste the recipes into that document to save.

Searching Other Recipe Sources

When searching through cookbooks, magazines, or emailed newsletters, apply the same steps to find your optimal recipes.

Magazines

If you decide to give a recipe from a magazine a try, tear the page out and place it in your file folder of recipes to try.

Cookbooks

MAKE YOUR OWN MIX

If a recipe you really want to make calls for any kind of highly processed ingredient, try substituting a homemade ingredient instead. For example, instead of using a packaged taco mix, create your own with spices you have at home (you can easily find a recipe online).

For cookbooks, browse through any you already own for specific types of dishes. For example, if you want to add a chicken recipe to the menu, look through the poultry section. Same with meat, pasta, dessert, etc. If you make the recipe and decide it's a keeper, type the recipe into a Word document and print it out or make a copy and place it in your "cookbook" (see chapter 5). If you don't have a problem tearing a recipe out of your cookbook, feel free to do so and put it in your "cookbook." For some reason, I can't seem to make myself do this.

Cooking Shows

Each week, check out what your favorite chefs are offering on their cooking shows. Record the shows that look interesting and decide whether you want to use any of their dishes for one of your weekly menu plans. Find the recipe online and print it, pin it online (I use Pinterest), or save it in your Word document.

Here are two recipe samples. The first is one I wouldn't recommend, because it has several ingredients that are too processed. The second is a similar version made with whole foods that I would steer you toward.

Version A (Avoid): Made-Up Chili Recipe

Ingredients:

- 1 pound ground beef
- 1 medium onion, chopped
- 1 can (16 ounces) kidney beans, rinsed and drained
- 1 can (15 ounces) black beans, rinsed and drained
- 1 can (15 ounces) pinto beans, rinsed and drained
- 1 can (14 1/2 ounces) diced tomatoes, undrained
- 1 can (10 ounces) diced tomatoes and green chiles
- 1 teaspoon chili powder
- 1 beef bouillon cube
- 1 can (11 1/2 ounces) V8 juice
- 2 envelopes ranch salad dressing mix
- 2 envelopes taco seasoning
- Sour cream, shredded cheddar cheese, and corn chips, optional

I'm not crazy about the prepared salad dressing, taco seasonings, V8 juice, or beef bouillon cube in this dish. All four are probably loaded with sodium and lots of preservatives.

Version B (Healthier Version): Ina Garten's Chicken Chili Recipe
(foodnetwork.com/recipes/ina-garten/chicken-chili-recipe/index.html)

Ingredients:

- 4 cups chopped yellow onions (3 onions)
- 1/8 cup good olive oil, plus extra for chicken
- 1/8 cup minced garlic (2 cloves)
- 2 red bell peppers, cored, seeded, and large-diced
- 2 yellow bell peppers, cored, seeded, and large-diced
- 1 teaspoon chili powder
- 1 teaspoon ground cumin
- 1/4 teaspoon dried red pepper flakes, or to taste
- 1/4 teaspoon cayenne pepper, or to taste
- 2 teaspoons kosher salt, plus more for chicken
- 2 cans (28 ounces each) whole peeled plum tomatoes in puree, undrained
- 1/4 cup minced fresh basil leaves
- 4 split chicken breasts, bone in, skin on
- Freshly ground black pepper

Everything used to make this dish is a natural, whole food. I've made it dozens of times, and it always gets rave reviews. If you notice, it has about the same amount of ingredients and takes about the same amount of time to make.

It may sound like it takes a lot of time to find recipes, but you will likely find that you can breeze through them

66

and quickly decide which ones to try. And with your healthier eating principles in mind, you'll be able to weed out many recipes very quickly.

Habit-Based Exercise for Finding Recipes

Week 1: Spend ten minutes one day this week searching your favorite cooking websites (or some I mentioned above) to find new recipes. Save recipes you want to try.

Week 2: Spend ten minutes one day this week searching through your cookbooks. Save recipes you want to try.

Week 3: (optional): Spend ten minutes one day this week searching through cooking magazines. Save recipes you want to try.

Week 4: (optional): Spend ten minutes one day this week searching through email newsletters. Save recipes you want to try.

Week 5: (optional): Spend ten minutes one day this week finding recipes from TV cooking shows. Save recipes you want to try.

If you choose to skip searching through magazines, email newsletters, or TV cooking shows, use weeks 3, 4, and 5 to continue finding recipes on cooking websites and in cookbooks.

Checklist for Finding Recipes

Add a checkmark for each time you successfully complete the action. Add an X for when you don't. *No judgment.* It's just a mark.

Week 1	Spend ten minutes searching websites for new recipes to try.	
Week 2	Spend ten minutes searching your cookbooks for recipes to try.	
Week 3	(*optional*) Spend ten minutes searching cooking magazines for recipes to try.	
Week 4	(*optional*) Spend ten minutes searching email newsletters for recipes to try.	
Week 5	(*optional*) Spend ten minutes finding recipes from TV cooking shows.	

Look at that. In one month, you could have dozens of new recipes to try.

Finding recipes doesn't have to be an aggravating process. You will eventually notice recipes everywhere. You might even dream them up in your sleep. And you'll quickly develop the ability to spot the ones you would enjoy adding to your collection. With an infinite number of recipes at your disposal, you'll rapidly rack up new ones to add to your "cookbook," making weekly meal planning that much easier.

Now that you've collected recipes (and are beginning to salivate), let's take a look at how to create your own "cookbook" so they're organized in a convenient place.

Chapter 5

CREATE YOUR VERY OWN "COOKBOOK"

Good cooking is an art which is easily acquired. There are only a few basic processes, and once they are mastered, even elaborate dishes seem simple to produce. No cookbook can provide the spark of genius, but it can serve as a source of inspiration and information.

—Fanny Farmer

Where is the recipe for those Thai pork lettuce wraps I loved? Did I find that online, or was it in one of my cookbooks? Nothing is more frustrating than not remembering where you put the recipe for something you really enjoyed. By storing your recipes in a faux "cookbook," you'll never have to worry about where you found them. This one-stop resource will prove invaluable when searching for recipes to put your weekly menus together.

I used to throw any recipes I found in magazines into a file folder. With no order to it, it eventually got so big and overwhelming that I never bothered to go through it. So my brilliant sister gave me the idea to build a personalized "cookbook." One year she bought me a binder and sheet protectors and told me to place recipes from

MY WELL-USED "COOKBOOKS"

magazines into the sheet protectors so I'd have one place to store them. I've accumulated hundreds upon hundreds of recipes over the years, and I always look through them first for meal ideas because only recipes I intend to cook again make it into the "cookbook." Thanks, JillyBean, for the wonderful idea!

Creating your own cookbook allows you to organize all the "keeper" recipes in one convenient location. By the end of this chapter, you'll be able to go directly to this resource to quickly find recipes for your weekly menus. I'll also tell you how to store recipes you've saved to try later.

Pretty soon, your cooking confidence level will soar, and your friends will be in awe of your new meal-planning abilities. And, be forewarned, they will probably start inviting themselves over for dinner. Trust me. When your friends ask what's for dinner and you rattle off, "I'm doing a dry-rubbed flank steak with balsamic onion relish and parmesan, oven-roasted green beans," you'll be fending them off every night.

Though your "cookbook" will take some time to grow, it should serve as your first source for finding recipes to include in your weekly menus.

Creating Your "Cookbook"

Supplies

Large three-ring binder or several smaller three-ring binders (I have two, two-inch binders)
Extra binder or file folder (I use a one-inch binder for this)
Two sets of dividers (preferably at least one of which has pockets)
Clear sheet protectors (the same size as your binder)
Recipes

Setup

Step 1 Gather your materials.
Step 2 Label dividers.
Step 3 Organize the dividers in binders.
Step 4 Place recipe in clear sheet protector.
Step 5 Add recipe to proper "cookbook" section.

Step 1: Gather Your Materials

When setting up your "cookbook" for the first time, bring together your binders, dividers, sheet protectors, and recipes you've accumulated from online, cookbooks, and other sources.

Step 2: Label Dividers

Label dividers with categories that make sense for you and your family. I have mine labeled as follows:

Poultry
Beef

Fish and Seafood
Pork
Lamb
Burgers and Sandwiches
Pasta, Rice, Grains, and Beans
Pizza, Breads, and Tarts
Vegetables and Sides
Soups and Stews
Breakfast Foods and Muffins
Dressing, Sauces, and Marinades
Appetizers, Drinks, and Desserts

You might also look in your favorite cookbooks to see how they've labeled theirs.

Step 3: Organize the Dividers in Binders

Place dividers in order, beginning with main dishes (like poultry, beef, fish and seafood, pork, etc.). You want to find the dishes you cook most often, especially the main courses, easily.

Step 4: Place Recipe in Clear Sheet Protector

Once you've cooked a recipe and decided you liked it enough to try it again, place it in a clear sheet protector. Sheet protectors not only help you organize, but they also keep your recipes clean because they're easy to wipe off.

Note: You can store two single-page recipes back to back in one sheet protector.

Step 5: Add Recipe
to Proper "Cookbook" Section

Within each section, organize the recipes by type of food. For instance, under the vegetable tab I have dozens of potato recipes, so I put them together, then the squash recipes, then green beans, etc. Under desserts, I put cookie recipes together, pie recipes in the same area, cake recipes together in another area, and so on.

Sometimes things will fit into two categories. If so, place it in the section that seems most logical to you so it's easy to find later.

Note: If you decide to keep a recipe you have stored anywhere online, in email, or your recipe Word document, print it out so you can store it in your "cookbook."

Setting Up Your "Recipes to Try" Binder

If you print out recipes you'd like to try in the future, keep those recipes in a separate folder/binder and don't place them in your "cookbook" until you've made them and decided to keep them. Otherwise, things get jumbled up, and you might not know which ones you've tried and liked.

Step 1	Label dividers
Step 2	Organize dividers in binder.
Step 3	Add recipe to proper section.
Step 4	Move "keeper" recipes to permanent "cookbook" section.

MAKE NOTES

Make notes in your recipes after you've made them. Sometimes I will add ingredients to a dish; in this case, I'll write those down somewhere in the recipe so I can remember to put those items on the grocery list when I plan to make the meal again. Making notes also allows you to remember something you've discovered about the recipe that you want to recall each time, like a cooking technique you learned or the exact amount of time it took. Or maybe one cup of cream was way too much for the dish. If you don't make a note, you might keep making the same mistake.

Your "cookbook" will serve as your first source when creating your weekly meal plans. Take pride in knowing it will

Step 1: Label Dividers

Take your second set of dividers and give them the same headings you used in your "cookbook."

Step 2: Organize Dividers in Binder

Place dividers in the extra binder or folder as you did for your cookbook.

Step 3: Add Recipe to Proper Section

Place untried recipes into the extra binder in the same order as your cookbook. If using dividers that have pockets, place each recipe in a pocket (I find it's easiest to use tabs with a pocket so your recipes aren't floating around and causing a big mess). If they don't have pockets, just place them in the sections as best as possible. No need to organize recipes by type of food (e.g. no need for a squash or broccoli section). A broader vegetable section should do the trick.

Step 4: Move "Keeper" Recipes to Permanent "Cookbook"

Once you've cooked the recipe, if you liked it and want to keep it, place it into a sheet protector and move it to your permanent "cookbook" so that it won't be lost.

be full of recipes you've tried and enjoyed—and full of whole foods. So, always keep adding to it. You don't need to add a new recipe every day or even every week, and as you progress and fill up your cookbook, you'll find you only need to add them every once in a while.

Habit-Based Exercise for Creating Your Cookbook

Week 1–Week 4: Add at least one new recipe to your "Recipes to Try" binder or folder each week.

Week 5 and beyond: Commit to trying one new recipe each week, and if you decide it's a keeper, place it in a sheet protector and add the recipe to your cookbook.

Moving forward, continue to keep an eye out for new recipes and organize them so that when you're meal planning, which you'll learn in the next chapter, there'll be lots to choose from.

Checklist for Creating Your Cookbook

Add a checkmark for each time you successfully complete the action. Add an X for when you don't. *No judgment*. It's just a mark.

Week	1	2	3	4
Add one new recipe to your "Recipes to Try" binder or folder.				

Week	5	6	7	8
Commit to trying one new recipe each week. Add keeper recipes to "cookbook."				

Now that you've accumulated recipes and started your "cookbook," let's use our resources and organized kitchens to turn our attention to the reason you bought this book: planning your weekly menus.

Chapter 6

DESIGN YOUR WEEKLY DINNER MENUS

The majority of people eat over a thousand meals a year and if a man lives a normal span he has some fifty sentient years in which to enjoy more than fifty thousand meals. This surely is a matter of some importance and worthy of considerable time and thought.

—Frank Oliver

As I said before, when I started cooking more frequently, I was basically making the same three to five meals every week and getting pretty tired of bland chicken served with boxed stuffing mix or starchy pasta loaded with creamy sauce and little protein. And the veggies were anemic. It took trial and error before I figured out how to generate new, exciting, and balanced meals every week, but now I smile when I look at my dry-erase board full of nutritious meals that I actually look forward to making (and eating).

It seems many are desperate to solve the annoying question of, "What's for dinner?" With good intentions and in hopes of finding something to make their food lives easier (and maybe a little healthier), many even turn to menu/meal-planning services, where customers receive prepared meals or meal kits and do a small amount of cooking to get dinner on the table. ("Help me, <Insert meal-kit delivery service here>; you're my only hope." If you're not a Star Wars fan, I apologize for the reference.) But time and time again, I hear from people who have burned out on these services, claiming that variety is lacking, which causes monotony and boredom.

And then cooking shows, magazines, and other sources are not terribly practical in terms of offering balanced meal ideas or full weekly menus. Ultimately, it's up to you to figure out how best to piece together an entire weekly plan, a task that can seem intimidating.

Planning menus is the crux of healthier eating because it makes getting nutritious meals on the table a lot easier. You know that eating "perfectly" doesn't exist, but having these balanced meals grace your table can, at a minimum, provide you with at least one great meal a day. And because you are the one who chooses what sounds good (from an infinite number of choices), it's unlikely you'll ever run out of options. So, monotony and boredom become a thing of the past.

Now that you're beginning to fill up your cookbook with healthier recipes and have a better idea of what balanced meals look like, you can put together nutritious menus on your own.

By the end of this chapter, you should feel more comfortable using resources you already have on hand to design weekly menus full of well-balanced meals. And once you have that plan visible and easily accessible, I hope you'll feel excited and inspired to create those meals. So let's get planning!

To get started with your weekly meal plans, you'll need:

- Pen or pencil and paper
- Dry-erase board, chalkboard, corkboard, and/or plain paper
- Your "cookbook"
- Extra folder of "Recipes to Try"
- Internet access, cookbooks, and cooking magazines (*optional*)

Creating Your Weekly Menu

Step 1   Gather materials.

Step 2   Take inventory.

Step 3   Consider plans.

Step 4   Choose recipes to create balanced meals and write out menu.

Step 5   Maker room for leftovers.

Step 6   Transfer menu (with instructions) to dry-erase board or fresh sheet of paper.

Step 7   Take a look at your menu daily.

Step 8   Cross meal off menu.

Step 1: Gather Materials

See list above.

Step 2: Take Inventory

What food do you already have that you may be able

to incorporate in your menu this week? Perhaps you bought extra chicken when it was on sale, and it's sitting in your freezer. Maybe you have food from your community-supported agriculture (CSA) in the pantry. Or, you ended up going out for dinner one night when you hadn't expected to, and now you have extra protein in the freezer. Maybe you already have some shrimp or salmon in the freezer. You don't need to buy more. As long as it's still fresh and safe to eat, what's on hand can be a great thing to add to your menu. Make a mental note or write out what you have in your fridge, freezer, and pantry that needs to be used before expiration.

Step 3: Consider Plans

What are your plans for the week, and how many meals will you be eating at home? How many people will you be feeding at each meal?

Step 4: Choose Recipes to Create Balanced Meals and Write Out Menu

First, decide how many nights you want to eat chicken, beef, fish, pasta, pork, vegetarian, etc. Remember to take your inventory list into account.

Next, use your inventory list to start searching through your recipes to find any that might use those ingredients.

Select recipes from your "cookbook" first since these are recipes you've tried and enjoyed.

To design balanced meals, start by going through the first few sections of your "cookbook" and choose a protein-based recipe, then go to the vegetable tab and pick something to complement that protein. You can either pick all your proteins at once and then go to the vegetable section, or you can toggle between the two as you try to make a complete meal.

I write my protein-based dish first, and then I write the veggie dish next to it. But sometimes, I'll switch up the vegetables, and I don't necessarily cook them in the order I write them down. If you choose to pick all your proteins first, write each one down and leave space to write down your veggie choice(s). Now you can add whole grain carbs to the menu (if you'd like). You probably don't need to focus too much on adding fat, as most dishes call for some kind of oil to cook with. But you can definitely consider dishes that have healthier fats (like avocados, fish, nuts, etc.). As

VEGETABLES

Don't be afraid to make veggies the star of the show by using recipes that highlight their flavors. If making elaborate protein dishes, cook simple vegetables by steaming or oven-roasting them. Or use an easy protein-based recipe and spend a little more time on veggies. Even if you're a vegetarian or vegan—perhaps especially if you are—or have other dietary restrictions, it's super important to choose recipes that are high in protein, because it's often harder for you to get a good amount of protein every day.

If you're making a dish that has protein and veggies together (like a stew), no need to worry about adding a separate vegetable dish (although adding another simple veggie dish to go with your main meal is rarely a bad idea).

Refer back to chapter 1 if you need a refresher on balanced meals, because this is where you'll want to spend your time when planning menus.

After you've looked through your cookbook, if you still need recipe ideas, use other resources and repeat the process.

If you haven't found a use for items on your inventory list, now may be a good time to go to a website like bigoven.com/recipes/leftover, which allows you to enter ingredients to generate a list of recipes that includes those items.

you go through your recipes, it may take a few tries and crossed-out lines to get your menu the way you want it.

Step 5: Make Room for Leftovers

Leftovers can make your week incredibly easy because they keep you from having to cook every night, so consider cooking more than you need and saving the rest for another evening. You can also take leftovers and create something entirely new from them. If using leftovers, be sure to write them down on your weekly menu.

(See page 91 for examples of turning leftovers into new meals.)

Step 6: Transfer Menu (with Instructions) to Dry-Erase Board or Fresh Sheet of Paper

As you're transferring your menu from your piece of paper to the dry-erase board or clean piece of paper, add any do-ahead instructions you might need to consider for your week. For example, if you need to thaw something, write that next to the menu item. If a recipe calls for marinating something, write that next to that menu item. If you need to precook something for a meal, write that on the menu.

Once you plan your weekly dinner menu, you can make your week as flexible as you want. If you have five or more protein-based recipes and five or more vegetable recipes, you can cook them based on what you're in the mood for that night. Some people like to do Taco Tuesdays or Leftover Sundays, etc. It's perfectly fine to look at your menu every day and decide what you feel like eating that evening. And once you consider your week, you'll have a better idea of when might be the best day to make certain meals. For example, a slow-cooker meal would work beautifully if you know you won't have time to cook after an evening workout or soccer game. If this is the case, you can write in parentheses what day you plan to cook that meal.

Note on thawing foods: Though you have flexibility, there is a caveat. If you've bought beef, chicken, and fish for the week, some of that protein will probably have to be frozen. In that case, you'll need to make sure to thaw those items before cooking. Just be sure to give yourself at least one day to let your protein thaw in the refrigerator. Write out on your dry-erase board when to take something out of the freezer. For example, if it's Monday and you know you're going to want chicken fajitas later in the week, write a note on the board to "take chicken out of freezer." And please, no quick thawing here. You can quick-thaw shrimp and bread, but most other foods, especially proteins, need at least twenty-four hours in the fridge to thaw. In general, chicken and meats can stay in the fridge for about two to three days while fish lasts one to two days. A simple smell test can help you detect when something has gone bad.

Step 7: Take a Look at Your Menu Daily

Check to see if any prep work needs to be done beforehand or when foods in the freezer need to be transferred to the refrigerator.

Step 8: Cross Meal off Menu

As you make each meal, cross through or delete them from your dry-erase board and give yourself a pat on the back, knowing that by cooking at home you're taking one of the biggest steps toward healthier eating habits.

Here are examples of a few weeks of meal plans at my house. Check out lisakschreiber.com for more plans and grocery lists.

Sample Meal Plan 1

Wasabi Pork Chops (protein), Oven-Roasted Potatoes with Veggies (optional carb and veggies), Salad with Homemade Vinaigrette (veggies and healthy fat)
Chicken Fajitas (protein), Sautéed Mushrooms and

Onions (veggies), Easy Homemade Guacamole (healthy fat), Spanish Rice (optional carb)

BBQ Chicken Sandwiches (protein and optional carb), Roasted Broccoli with Parmesan and Pine Nuts (veggie, healthy fat)

Meatloaf (protein), Salad (veggie), Oven-Roasted Sweet Potato Fries (optional carb)

Salmon Kebabs (protein) with Grilled Squash and Zucchini (veggies)

Quick Quiche (protein), Salad with Homemade Honey Mustard Dressing (veggie, healthy fat)

Leftover Quiche (protein), Chicken Sausages (protein), Spicy Shallot Brussels Sprouts (veggies, healthy fat)

Note: I added in the macronutrient to this first menu just so you can get a sense of how I try to balance my meals. You don't need to worry about adding that to your menu.

Sample Meal Plan 2

Asian-Style Sea Bass, Cauliflower with Asian Flavors

Spicy Pork Tenderloin with Ginger-Maple Sauce, Spinach Salad with Goat Cheese, Sunflower Seeds, Dried Cranberries

Meathead Taco Salad with Avocados, Black Olives, Tomatoes, and Homemade Vinaigrette

Pan-Seared Chicken Breast with Shallot Pan Sauce, Green Bean "Fries"

Zucchini and Goat Cheese Frittata, Oven-Roasted Brussels Sprouts with Sea Salt

Cilantro-Lime Chicken with Avocado Salsa, Kale Salad, Quinoa

Dry-Rubbed Flank Steak, Balsamic Onion Relish, Spicy Balsamic Sautéed Mushrooms

Sample Meal Plan 3
(with Instructions Included)

Goat Cheese–Stuffed Chicken, Cauliflower Rice, Sautéed Mushrooms

Stir-Fry Quinoa with Shrimp, Broccoli with Chili and Garlic

Salmon on Spinach Salad with Goat Cheese, Avocado, Tomatoes, Onions, Mushrooms, Hard-Boiled Eggs, Sunflower Seeds **(Take Salmon out of Freezer.)**

Spicy Chicken Sandwiches, Baked Sweet Potato Fries, Shaved Brussels Sprouts **(Take Chicken out of Freezer.)**

Spicy Chipotle Chicken Stew, Spinach Salad with Warm Bacon Vinaigrette **(Make Stew ahead in Slow Cooker.)**

Grilled Beef Kebabs, "Candied" Corn, Kale Salad **(Marinate Meat.)**

Spicy Tortilla Soup, Salad with Grilled Shrimp **(Take Shrimp out of Freezer.)**

Here's a peek at one of my dry-erase menus:

Don't get overwhelmed with my sample meal plans. I really love to cook, so I usually prefer making a new meal most evenings and reserving my leftovers for lunches. And the recipes are actually easier than they sound. It takes me only a few minutes to put these lists together because I've thought about what types of meals I want for the week. And because I've been doing this for so long, I have a pretty good idea of the recipes I want to use. I still search for new recipes all the time. It is, in fact, a bit of an obsession for me. So I'm constantly adding new meals to my collection.

Meal Formulas

If the dishes above seem complicated, try using the following meal "formulas" to put together dishes that naturally complement each other.

Choose One from Each Column

Protein/ Main Dish	Vegetable	High-Fiber Carb (Optional)
Chicken	Brussels Sprouts	Quinoa
Beef	Broccoli or Cauliflower	Whole Wheat Couscous
Pork	Leafy Green Veggie (Kale, Lettuce, Etc.)	Beans
Lamb	Squash/Zucchini	Whole Wheat Bread
Fish	Green Beans (or Edamame)	Farrow
Beans, Legumes	Peppers	Brown Rice
Eggs	Carrots	Whole Grain Pasta
Shrimp	Mushrooms	Bulgur
	Tomatoes	Barley
	Asparagus	Corn
		Potato or sweet potato

The more you do this, the more you will be able to identify what food combinations you like, and you'll probably find yourself making up some of your own.

Turning Leftovers into New Meals

Sloppy Joes or other ground-beef dishes can become chili if you add cheese, avocados, tortilla chips, and sour cream.

Leftover marinated flank steak or chicken can be used to fill flour tortillas with sautéed onions and mushrooms for taco or burrito night. Or turn them into quesadillas by adding tortillas with cheese and pan-frying them in a touch of olive oil.

Take leftover, cold mashed potatoes and lightly fry them in a little canola oil for potato patties. Serve with steak or grilled chicken and/or green veggie.

Cooked chicken can be used in an infinite number of leftover dishes. Turn a basic pan-seared chicken breast into a pasta dish with an easy dressing or olive oil and parmesan cheese. Take chicken you made for fajitas and serve it over rice, couscous, quinoa, or another pantry staple.

Leftover fish can be turned into fish tacos with home-made guacamole.

Turn leftover meatloaf into meatloaf sandwiches.

Take leftover marinated chicken you used for fajitas one night and use it for a fancier salad with lots of veggies and a few hard-boiled eggs for some extra protein.

REMEMBER, IT'S ABOUT THE BASICS

Don't get hung up on details and lose sight of the forest for the trees. For example, if you want cheese with your hamburger, don't stress about what nutrients are in that cheese. Just make sure you're starting with healthier basics like lean protein and veggies.

Get creative and make up your own ideas for repurposing leftovers. And check out my website for new examples. Also, if you're so inclined, come to my website to send me your ideas for leftovers.

Non–Recipe Users

You don't have to follow recipes, but you do have to plan.

For those of you who prefer to be alchemists in the kitchen, conjuring up your own recipes from scratch, don't fret. I applaud you, and quite frankly, I'm a little jealous of your ingenuity. Simply follow the instructions on setting up your menus and then make sure your grocery list includes all the ingredients you need to make your meals. I still advocate adding one or two new recipes (or concoctions) a week so you'll constantly be growing your collection. You don't want to burn out on the same five or six meals. If you don't plan your menus, you will likely find yourself at the store several days a week making last-minute grocery runs or getting takeout more than you'd prefer. If you don't mind doing frequent shopping or eating fast food, you've probably wasted your money on this book.

If you find yourself getting bored because you're making the same meals every week, try browsing one of the many internet food websites just for ideas. Then get creative and make your own version of the same meal. You don't have to follow a recipe, but you do have to have the ingredients on hand (see chapter 3 for well-stocked kitchen ideas) to be sure you can make a complete meal.

You can also check out chapter 8, in which I offer specific ingredients that are found in certain types of cuisines. For example, ingredients with Asian flavors might include soy sauce, hoisin, sweet and sour sauces, green onions, fish sauce, wasabi, or sesame oil. If you want to make a dish with a certain flavor profile, this might be a good starting point.

Even if you prefer not using recipes, consider writing down the ingredients and amounts when making a meal you've never made before. Otherwise, you may love it and never be able to duplicate it. (That's my mom's specialty.)

Don't forget, though, the healthier eating rules apply to you too. Make sure the bulk of your ingredients are whole foods. And you should still go ahead and make out a complete grocery list. Otherwise, you might buy items you think will be good for a dish and then end up throwing them away without ever using them. It's also more tempting to throw unhealthy items in your cart when you go in without a list.

On a vacation several years ago, I serendipitously ended up in a cooking demonstration about taste taught by a charismatic woman named Barb Stuckey. I highly recommend her book, *Taste What You're Missing: The Passionate Eater's Guide to Why Good Food Tastes Good*, for terrific ideas on how to balance your dishes so they have the right flavor combinations. You can also check out *Ratio: The Simple Codes Behind the Craft of Everyday Cooking* by Michael Ruhlman for guidance on using fundamental ingredients and techniques to make meals.

Meal Planning for CSA and Local Farmers Markets

I enjoy the small market near my home (open only on Wednesdays) where local farmers sell their fresh produce. Because availability is unpredictable, I can't always plan my meals around it. But I love buying their fresh foods, so I sometimes stop by before my weekly meal-planning session and purchase veggies that look good; then I incorporate those into my plans. Oftentimes, I'll use their fresh produce for my lunches and save my fruits and veggies from my favorite permanent farmers market for dinners—a vegetable double whammy.

If you are part of a CSA or like to shop for fresh fruits and veggies from a local market, you can incorporate these sources into your meal planning just fine. With a well-stocked kitchen and some practice, this is quite doable. I see several ways to go about this. Pick out what looks good at the market before you do your general grocery shopping for the week and you'll know what you need to add to the grocery list to make complete dishes. Or, if you want to buy the majority of your veggies through a CSA or local farmers market, just make sure to buy enough for the whole week and use simple techniques to emphasize those fresh vegetables. Oven-roasted veggies are a cinch, require few ingredients (you likely have olive oil, salt, and pepper), and taste delicious. After all, you want to highlight the taste of fresh produce, not mask it with other elements. So keep it simple. You'll find endless ways to utilize fresh veggies, and we've already established that they are an extremely important part of the healthier eating process. So don't skip them.

* * *

You may fall out of the menu-planning habit every now and then. Give yourself a break. Start over the next day or the next week. But do start over. Pretty soon, you might find you don't enjoy eating out as much as you used to. (You may already be feeling that way.) You'll surely appreciate dining out more if it becomes a treat instead of an everyday event.

When you've come up with your own meal plans for a few weeks, email them to me at lisa@lisakschreiber.com. Show off your hard-earned skills. I know I'm going to be impressed.

But first, let me offer a menu-planning habit exercise and checklist to get you cooking. It may take a very long time to work up to cooking five to seven dinners a week, so keep the expectations low and the curiosity level high as you figure out what works for you. And just keep plugging away.

Habit-Based Exercise for Planning Weekly Dinner Menus

Week 1: Plan and cook one dinner this week.

Week 2: Plan and cook two dinners this week.

Week 3: Plan and cook three dinners this week.

Week 4: Plan and cook four dinners this week.

Weeks 5 and on: Plan and cook five to seven dinners.

Checklist for Planning
Weekly Dinner Menus

Add a checkmark for each time you successfully complete the action. Add an X for when you don't. *No judgment*. It's just a mark.

		S	M	T	W	T	F	S
Week 1	Plan and cook one dinner this week.							
Week 2	Plan and cook two dinners this week.							
Week 3	Plan and cook three dinners this week.							
Week 4	Plan and cook four dinners this week.							
Week 5	Plan and cook five or more dinners this week.							
Week 6	Plan and cook five or more dinners this week.							

Now that you've put all this work into planning your menus, you certainly don't want to spend an obscene amount of time at the grocery store/farmers market or have to make more than one trip a week. Next, we'll learn to streamline that trip so you get what you need fast and with as little frustration as possible.

Chapter 7

GENERATE A KICK-ASS GROCERY LIST

I have never written anything in one draft,
not even a grocery list, although I have heard from
friends that this is actually possible.
—Connie Willis

On a recent trip to my local grocery store, I noticed the layout had completely changed and no longer came close to the template I was using to make my weekly trips more manageable. Panic set in. Okay, it didn't. But frustration sure did. Then a nice employee, who saw me looking puzzled, asked me if I'd like a list of the new layout. Would I ever!

I know very few people who wish to spend large blocks of time at the grocery store. My dad was a rare exception to this. I have to be honest here. As much as I love my meal-planning system, I despise going to the grocery store and my local, permanent farmers market. And yet, I'm there consistently. Every. Single. Week.

When Webvan started delivering groceries in my area many years ago, we were among the first to sign up. In my book, that was one of the greatest services ever invented. Unfortunately, the company was way before its time and didn't last long. So, once again, I started making my weekly trek to the big-box stores. If your hatred of grocery shopping is keeping you from cooking at home, by all means invest a little extra money in having groceries delivered. This could also be helpful in curbing the habit of throwing impulse buys (and potentially less-nutritious, red-light items) into your cart. Cooking at home with whole foods is worth every penny, so if paying a small amount in delivery fees will get you cooking, then by all means do it.

As I honed my system, I knew had to figure out how to get in and out of those stores efficiently because I didn't want to waste my time there.

I know some prefer to shop by what looks good at the market. And the more experience you have with meal planning, the more likely you are to be successful at this because you'll know what you have at home to make that work. But in the meantime, studies show that an overwhelming number of choices can cause anxiety and depression. With a grocery list, you take those choices out of the equation. You might find that you actually love the freedom of not looking at the ridiculously huge cereal selection or having to choose between fifty types of jarred pasta sauces. Peace of mind is a big deal.

By the end of this chapter, you'll know how to arrange your items in a simple spreadsheet or app so you can maneuver the market efficiently and get in and out as quickly as possible. Knowing you won't have to spend an inordinate amount of time at the store makes it easier to get it done every week.

Getting Set Up

Create or Obtain a Store Directory

Ask the customer service center for a store directory. Or take pen and paper on your next trip and use the store signs as a guide to write down what's on every aisle according to how you shop the store. You can also snap a picture of the signs in each aisle that display the contents of that aisle. You may think you look silly doing this, but I guarantee you'll be having the last laugh when you see that guy grunting about having to go back to the produce section when you're both in the dairy aisle.

And, you only have to do this once, unless your store reorganizes, to have a template for efficient shopping.

Create Your Spreadsheet

You have several options here. You can use or modify my spreadsheet (lisakschreiber.com/the-meal-deal-book), create your own spreadsheet, or use an app like Grocery iQ.

If using my spreadsheet, make sure it's laid out based on how you prefer to shop the store. For example, at the grocery store I frequent—and most of their stores are laid out the same way—the first aisle I visit contains the fresh produce, bakery, specialty cheeses, and deli counter sections. I always save the milk, butter, and frozen-food section for last so those foods stay cold. If you have a different approach, modify my sheet to meet your needs.

If your spreadsheet/app allows you to rearrange the layout, do so based on how you shop the store. If not,

GROCERY APPS

Apps can make grocery organization so much easier. For example, your local store might have one. But I'm still pretty old school. I like to print my list at home and read from it at the store. (I'm also one of the remaining few who prefers to read an actual book rather than a tablet computer or e-reader.) Other terrific, free grocery apps for iOS and Android are Grocery Pal, Out of Milk, and AnyList.

don't worry. Just make sure to go over your list before you check out to make sure you're not forgetting anything.

Once you have your spreadsheet/app set up, you will not need to regenerate a new list every week. You can make a master template for your shopping list and name it something like "Master Grocery Template." Each week, open your master template and save it as a different file. I save mine as the date I'm going shopping. For example, I create a new file folder where I store a "Master Grocery Template." Each week, I open that file, add my items, and then save it as the date I'm shopping (for instance, 10/10/2019).

If you have staple items that you buy every week, such as milk, eggs, tomatoes, kale, brussels sprouts, etc., type them into the master template so those items always appear on the list.

Tip: Consider adding some kind of fresh lettuce each week to your master template so you'll always have ingredients to put together some kind of salad with dinner if you're lacking a veggie.

Create Your Weekly Shopping List

Step 1   Keep paper and pen in the kitchen.

Step 2   Gather materials.

Step 3   Add weekly dinner menu ingredients to grocery list.

Step 4   Add items from the grocery list to their proper section on the spreadsheet or app.

Step 1: Keep Paper and Pen in the Kitchen

As needed, write down staple items to replenish on your next grocery trip. You should be doing this all week as you start to run out of things. Include things like breakfast ingredients, lunch and/or snack foods, paper goods, cleaning and personal items, etc.

Step 2: Gather Materials

Materials include the following:

- Grocery list with staple items
- Prepared spreadsheet, grocery store app, or my spreadsheet (lisakschreiber.com/the-meal-deal-book)
- Recipes you plan to use for the week

Step 3: Add Weekly Dinner Menu Ingredients to Grocery List

Go through each recipe for the week and add needed ingredients to your grocery list.

Step 4: Add Items from the Grocery List to Their Proper Section on the Spreadsheet or App

Once your grocery store layout is in a spreadsheet, smartphone app, or other format and you've made out your weekly menu and added ingredients you'll need to your grocery list, start transferring items from your paper list to your spreadsheet or app in their proper section. So apples would go under "produce," bread under "bakery," eggs under "dairy," steaks under "meat," and so on.

And remember to write down the amount of an item you'll need. It's no fun to get to the store and realize you don't know how much cheddar cheese you need and have to guess. You don't need to write down quantities if you're only getting one. For example, if whole wheat bread is on your list, no need to write "one" for the quantity—unless you need more than one. But if you're buying more than one item, put the quantity needed (e.g. green peppers (2), or 1/2 cup cheddar cheese).

Though this whole process takes a few extra minutes, you'll be thrilled with how much time and frustration you save on your next store visit.

I'll share an example of how my grocery list looks when shopping at my local stores. This invaluable list saves me frustration, and it has garnered me several "wows" from fellow grocery store patrons.

Example Grocery List

Grocery Store	Farmers Market
Breads/Bakery	Chocolates
Pastrami	
Whole Wheat English Muffins	**Nuts**
Produce	**Soft Drinks, Juices**
Avocados (2)	Virgil's Root Beer
Bananas (4)	Organic Apple Juice
Pasta/Rice/Canned Fish	**Oils**
	Large, Organic Olive Oil
Canned Vegetables/Fruits/Salad Dressings	
Condiments/International Foods	**Canned Foods**
Small Black Olives	28-Ounce Can Whole Fire-Roasted Tomatoes
	Flours, Pastas, Rice
Cereal/Peanut Butter/Jams/Syrup	Chia Seeds
	Alcohol
Potato Chips/Candy/Cookies/Nuts	
	Spices
Poultry	Paprika
	Herbs
Fish	Mint
	Produce
Meat	Tomatoes
	Spinach
	Artichokes (2)

Baking Aisle/Cooking Oil/Crackers/Vinegar	Romaine
	Onions
Coffee/Tea	Butternut Squash
	Bok Choy
Soups	Cucumber
	Organic Iceberg
Laundry/Cleaning Supplies	Kale
	Sweet Potato
Foil Pans/Wraps/Napkins/Paper Plates	Russet Potato
	Mushrooms
Bath Tissue/Paper Towels	Green Beans
	Corn
Greeting Cards	Cilantro
	Green Pepper (2)
Bar Soap/Hair Products/Cosmetics	Ginger
	Green Onions
Energy Drinks	Cauliflower
	Red Potatoes (1/2 Lb.)
Soft Drinks	Asparagus
	Yellow Squash (2)
Juices	Brussels Sprouts
	Okra
Powdered Beverages/Sport Drinks	
	Fruits
Beer/Ice/Water	Grapefruit
	Oranges (2)
Milk/Butter	Pineapple
Chocolate Milk	Grapes
OJ	Strawberries
	Lemons (2)

Eggs/Egg Substitutes	Breads
	Whole Wheat Sourdough
Dairy/Cheeses	
	Coffee
Frozen Foods	
Frozen Blueberries	**Fish**
	Cocktail Sauce
Household Products	Tuna
Gallon, Quart Storage Bags	Salmon
	Cooked Shrimp
Miscellaneous	
	Poultry
	Chicken (2)
	Bone-In, Skin-On Chicken (2)
	Meats
	1/2 Lb. Grass-Fed Ground Sirloin
	Pork Tenderloin
	Cheeses
	Parmesan Cheese
	Cheddar Cheese
	Dairy
	Sour Cream
	2% Milk
	Eggs
	Jerky
	Greek Yogurt

You'll notice that the produce section at the farmers market is by far the most extensive category on my list. Think that's a coincidence for a healthy-eating meal planner? I think not. But also notice that I have a few slightly processed items. Remember, we're going for 80 percent, not perfect.

Tip: Take your headphones and plug into your smartphone so you can listen to tunes or a podcast to take your mind off shopping.

Unless you just love spending time at the grocery store, use this process to get your shopping done quickly, and it will soon become just another weekly habit. Making grocery shopping more bearable is worth it because it can have an enormous impact on your eating lifestyle.

And speaking of habits, here's your habit-based exercise and checklist for putting together a shopping list and going to the market.

Habit-Based Exercise for Making Your Shopping List

Week 1 and beyond: Take your handy paper grocery list and add the items to their proper place in your spreadsheet, app, or whatever organization method you plan to take shopping. You can do this any day, or every day, of the week, as long as you're regularly adding items. Once you transfer your paper list to the spreadsheet or app, you no longer need the paper list. Next week you can start with a clean piece of paper.

Checklist for Making Your Shopping List

Add a checkmark for each time you successfully complete the action. Add an X for when you don't. *No judgment.* It's just a mark.

Week	1	2	3	4	5
Add items to your list and get shopping.					

Now that you've zipped through the store and are ready to get home and cook, it's time to take your new efficiency skills and transfer them to your kitchen so you don't end up wasting lots of time preparing meals.

Chapter 8

PREP MEALS LIKE A PRO

I'm a good cook, and I look at something like Iron Chef *and think, "It's a good thing I already know how to cook"—because I would never think I could do it if I watched these shows.*
—Nora Ephron

When I started cooking more consistently, each part of the meal rarely finished cooking at the same time. Food would get cold. I'd be running around the kitchen dazed and confused, unsure of what I should be doing next. It's a wonder I didn't give up and order in. But back then, we had few meal-delivery service options, and I didn't want to get into the car and drive to a restaurant, which is probably one reason I stuck with cooking at home.

TV chefs make it look so easy. But I'm not gonna lie; it took time not to feel like a novice in the kitchen. The truth is, it doesn't matter if you screw up—even if it's forever, which it won't be. You're still doing yourself a world of good just by trying. I tell you this so that if you are trying to make changes you'll understand it doesn't happen overnight. And no one can tell you exactly how it should be done because it can be done any way you like.

But I also want you to know that I changed my food life by trying different things and figuring out what worked for me. In fact, I still play around with it. Have a growth mindset and a playful attitude, and things will fall into place.

Creating menus and cooking is like a puzzle. Figuring out what foods go well together, preparing dishes so that they're done at the same time, and having everything in efficient order so you can swiftly move around the kitchen is the key to solving that puzzle. The more you do it, the better and faster you become. And you might even come to enjoy the process.

Now, my husband praises my kitchen efficiency and how expeditiously I glide from stovetop to range to fridge to pantry. This has come from years of making meals, and it's something I'm proud to have put in the time and effort to learn. Being capable in this area makes you less likely to dread cooking meals at home. Once you know where to find things easily in the kitchen and learn to create delicious meals, your kitchen confidence will expand exponentially too.

By the end of this chapter, you'll know how to prep to make meals quickly. When you finish faster, you can get back to more pressing matters, like reading a good book or spending time with friends and family. And eventually, moving around your kitchen like a seasoned chef will come more naturally.

Become a Master Meal Prepper

Step 1   Read through all recipes.

Step 2   Prioritize timing.

Step 3   Prepare *mise en place*.

Step 4   Clean as you go.

Step 5   Check food for doneness and seasoning.

Step 6   *Mangia!*

Step 1: Read through All Recipes

Read through the entire recipe for all recipes you planned for that meal before beginning, then read through them again. As you go along, always be thinking about your next step.

Step 2: Prioritize Timing

Determine which recipe has the longest cooking time and start it first. Continue to read recipes as you go so you'll know when to start prepping the other recipes in your meal.

Note: Timing your meals so each component is ready at the same time is going to take some practice, so don't beat yourself up. When I started cooking, having my dishes come out at different times was a nightly occurrence. The potatoes would be ice cold by the time the steak was finished. You're going to botch this a few times, so don't worry too much about it. Keep at it and you'll get it down. If you read all your recipes carefully before you start cooking and think about the proper sequence, you will quickly learn how to avoid dishes going cold while waiting for the entire meal to be finished. And don't forget, you can place items in your oven at a very low temperature to keep them warm until ready to serve. Or, you may have a "hold warm" setting on your oven or microwave.

Step 3: Prepare *Mise en Place*

Get out the cutting boards and/or utensils you'll need for your dishes and pre-chop your ingredients. The French call it *mise en place*, "everything in its place." It's essential for timing your meals and preventing burnt foods and other kitchen mishaps. Ever had burnt garlic? Ick.

Mise en place basically comes down to having all your foods chopped up and ready to go. You also want all other ingredients readily available, like vinegars, oils, spices, etc. If you have ten minutes while your onions are cooking, you probably have time to cut up other ingredients, but I recommend having everything chopped prior to cooking, at least in the beginning. It all takes about the same amount of time, but you're less likely to burn garlic and other delicate ingredients if you have everything ready to go. As you become a more seasoned cook, you may feel more comfortable eliminating the *mise en place*. But I still chop most of my ingredients before I even start cooking because something often goes wrong if I don't.

If a recipe calls for you to add carrots, celery, potatoes, and garlic at the same time, prep everything, and put it in one bowl. If it calls for adding the garlic later, put the garlic in a separate little dish or ramekin. Small glass or silicon bowls are ideal and easy to clean.

Also, check for overlapping ingredients in your recipes. Need it twice, chop it once. If you're using two recipes that call for the same ingredient, like onions or garlic, take this into consideration and chop enough for both dishes. Again, using ramekins can be helpful here. Portion out what you'll need for each dish, and then it's ready to go when you need it.

Step 4: Clean as you Go

As your meals are cooking and you find yourself standing around with not much to do but wait, clean a few dishes or put them in the dishwasher. You'll be surprised how little clean-up is left to do if you stay on top of it as you go.

Step 5: Check for Doneness and Seasoning

Keep a watchful eye on

MEASUREMENTS

Don't worry about measuring everything perfectly. You're not baking, which does require a certain degree of precision, so don't concern yourself with exactness at all times. For example, if a recipe calls for two tablespoons of olive oil to sauté something, you can easily eyeball enough oil to coat the pan. If a recipe calls for one cup of onions, just chop up about what you think a cup looks like (and you can add more if you love the ingredient). If a recipe calls for one teaspoon of Worcestershire or sriracha but you adore those flavors, just add what looks good. No need to pull out a measuring spoon every time. I rarely measure exact amounts of ingredients. It's very unlikely that a little more or less of an item will screw up your dish. If you don't follow the recipe to a T, it is almost always okay.

each dish and check to make sure things aren't over-browning, overcooking, or turning black. I depend on a timer to help me remember each dish. And use your sense of smell to make sure nothing's burning. Smell can be a great indicator that food is done cooking. The nose knows.

Taste and season as you go. It is amazing how layers of seasoning—especially salt and pepper—make all the difference between bold and bland dishes. Remember, though, not to taste any kind of raw meat or poultry. This includes tasting sauces if the meat/poultry isn't cooked through.

Tip: Use the oven light instead of opening the oven to check on your food. The temperature really does drop every time you open it.

Step 6: *Mangia!*

Enjoy the fruits of your labor.

Let Mistakes Be Your Friends

Once your kitchen is well stocked and organized and everything you need is in place, you'll be surprised how you zoom through the cooking process. Keep in mind that mistakes are part of that process (every single one of us makes them), so use them to learn what works best instead of getting upset, because that's how you eventually take command of your kitchen.

Tip: Taking a knife course at your local cooking store or watching videos online are great ways to learn knife skills. And feeling comfortable using a knife is imperative if you're going to put your cooking skills to good use.

Habit-Based Exercise for Prepping Meals

Week one and beyond: Read recipes all the way through before you start. Prep items you'll need for each recipe before you start cooking (wash, chop, peel, grate, etc.). Have all the ingredients ready to go before you even put anything on the stove or grill or in the oven. Get used to doing this and you can play with timing once you become more comfortable. You may only knock this habit out a few nights, or less, each week when you're getting started, and that's okay! Just focus on getting familiar with your recipe and handling the prep work for your meals.

Checklist for Prepping Meals

Add a checkmark for each time you successfully complete the action. Add an X for when you don't. *No judgment.* It's just a mark.

		S	M	T	W	T	F	S
Week 1	Read recipes, *mise en place.*							
Week 2	Read recipes, *mise en place.*							
Week 3	Read recipes, *mise en place.*							

		S	M	T	W	T	F	S
Week 4	Read recipes, *mise en place.*							
Week 5	Read recipes, *mise en place.*							
Week 6	Read recipes, *mise en place.*							

Most important with food/meal prep is to relax and not take it so seriously. Things will fall into place pretty quickly if you keep at it. Just taking the time to put together meals with fresh ingredients will instantly make you a better cook, not to mention what it could do for your health (and perhaps your sanity).

Once you get some practice with meal prep, precooking some of your items can go a long way toward cooking faster meals. It can also keep your fridge stocked full of more nutritious options for breakfast and/or lunch. So next, I'm going to offer ideas for simple foods you can make ahead when you have a little spare time.

Chapter 9

PRECOOK FOODS IN YOUR SPARE TIME

You don't have to be a chef or even a particularly good cook to experience proper kitchen alchemy: the moment when ingredients combine to form something more delectable than the sum of their parts. Fancy ingredients or recipes not required; simple, made-up things are usually even better.
—Erin Morgenstern

Sometimes when I'd get home from the gym in the evening, I'd pull out a recipe and realize it called for cooking something forty-five minutes before making the rest of the meal. It would drive me batty because I had planned to cook that meal in thirty minutes or less. Often I would scrap the meal entirely, and we'd grab something out. I found this was also happening when I would try to throw together a nutritious lunch in a hurry.

So I started using my weekly meal-planning time to think ahead about what I could precook so that wouldn't happen again. Not only was it a great idea to pre-make some things for dinners, but those same things could be turned into grab-and-go snacks or quick lunches as well. Bonus!

I played with making foods ahead of time so that all I had to do was grab them out of the fridge and eat them as they were or spend just a few minutes adding them to a salad or something easy. And now when I open the fridge and remember I already made something nutritious, I can chow down right away. It puts a smile on my face.

By the end of this chapter, you'll have some ideas for super simple make-ahead foods that can be used for breakfasts, lunches, snacks, backup meals—I'll talk more about those in the next chapter—and/or dinners. This will make it easier to stay on the healthier eating path because you'll have nutritious, already prepared foods waiting for you in the fridge.

While precooking foods is completely optional, it can go a long way toward ensuring you have your own version of fast food, only a lot healthier than the takeout kind. And you don't even have to leave the house to get it—or tip the delivery driver.

Ideas for Prep-Ahead Foods (and Ways to Use Them)

You can find many of these prep-ahead food ideas on my YouTube channel. And if you need some help determining safe cooking temperatures, check out this cool chart at www.foodsafety.gov/food-safety-charts/safe-minimum-cooking-temperature.

Proteins

Remember, these proteins can easily be added to

spinach or some kind of lettuce for an easy salad or to a tortilla for a great wrap.

Oven-Baked Shrimp

Place fresh or thawed peeled shrimp (or you can also take them directly from the freezer and dump them in a bowl of cool water—they'll be thawed in ten to fifteen minutes) on a rimmed baking sheet lined with foil or nonstick foil. Drizzle enough olive oil to coat the shrimp and add some lemon juice, salt, and pepper. Bake at 350 degrees for five minutes; flip the shrimp and bake another five minutes. Store in the fridge in an airtight container for up to three days.

Ideas for use: Serve with cocktail sauce for a snack or place on a salad or in a wrap with veggies for lunch or dinner.

Oven-Roasted Chicken

This is an extremely versatile item and a wonderful addition to your fridge. It's probably the item I make most often because it can be used in so many different ways. Roasting the chicken with the skin on and the bone in keeps it moist and yummy. And it couldn't be simpler to prepare.

Preheat oven to 350 degrees. On a foil-covered, rimmed baking sheet, rub skin-on, bone-in chicken breasts with olive oil, sprinkle with salt and pepper, and roast in the oven about forty-five minutes or until cooked through (a thermometer should read 165 degrees). Let cool. Remove skin and either store whole or cut the chicken off the breast and dice it into cubes or shred it, depending on what you plan to do with it. Store in fridge for several days.

Ideas for use: Use it in place of rotisserie chicken if called for in a recipe. Add it to a main dish or salad for some extra protein. It makes for a delightful chicken salad if you add a little mayo, celery, garlic powder, onion powder, salt, and pepper. Throw together a wrap with some veggies and salsa. Scramble eggs and add some chicken just before they set. Or just eat it plain if you need some protein in a hurry.

Hard-Boiled Eggs

Everyone has their own theory about how to make hard-boiled eggs. If you have a favorite, feel free to stick to it. If not, here's mine.

Place cold eggs into a saucepan that just fits the amount of eggs you want to boil. Add water to just above the top of the eggs. Bring to a boil. Reduce heat to medium and continue to boil for twenty minutes. Drain water and immediately place eggs in an ice bath (a bowl filled with ice and cold water) to stop them from cooking any more. The ice bath is a really important part of the process because it makes the eggs ridiculously easier to peel. Store unpeeled eggs in the fridge for up to a week. Peeled eggs should be eaten immediately.

Ideas for use: Hard-boiled eggs make for a great snack. Or create an egg salad (chop hard-boiled eggs and add mayo, mustard, relish, salt, and pepper) and serve on toasted whole wheat bread or crackers. You can also chop the eggs and add to a salad for extra protein.

Nitrate-Free Sausage

Purchase nitrate-free, less-processed sausages (we like chicken) and bake them at 350 degrees until cooked through, about twelve to fourteen minutes per side or per package directions. Store in an airtight container in the fridge for four to five days.

Ideas for use: Slice and serve in a salad or with another leafy vegetable. They make a great snack for a boost of protein. Or, add them to scrambled eggs or frittata.

Steak

Create a simple dry rub or use one of your homemade seasoning mixes (see spice section below) and rub it on a flank steak, flat iron steak, skirt steak, etc. Grill or broil for about five to seven minutes per side, until it reaches a temp of at least 145 degrees for medium rare. Let rest for ten minutes. Slice thin. Store steak in an airtight container in the fridge for up to four to five days.

Ideas for use: Steak can add protein to a simple salad or to a wrap with some veggies. Make a quick quesadilla by sandwiching steak, cheese, and veggies in a tortilla and cooking in a shallow pan on the stovetop (flip once to brown both sides). Or even just eat the steak as a snack instead of grabbing a protein bar.

Pork Tenderloin

You can cook pork tenderloin similar to your technique for cooking steak. Rub with your choice of seasoning mix, pan-sear on all sides for several minutes, then bake for twelve to fifteen minutes at 425 degrees until a thermometer reads 145 degrees. Let rest for ten minutes.

Store in an airtight container in the fridge for up to four to five days.

Ideas for use: Create an easy sandwich with whole wheat bread and vegetables (add condiments of your choice) or eat it in slices when you need a quick, high-protein snack.

Protein Smoothies

Smoothies can make a great addition to your daily eating habits because they're super fast to put together, and it's easy to make them balanced with protein, veggies, fruits, and healthy fats. They're also wonderful to make ahead and store in the fridge.

Here are my two favorites; we make these often in my house:

Banana protein smoothie (1 serving): Add 3/4 cup almond milk (I use either unsweetened vanilla or unsweetened chocolate), about 1/2 cup ice, 1 scoop protein powder (I use a vanilla whey powder), 1 banana, 1 teaspoon chia seeds, 1 teaspoon peanut butter, 1 teaspoon peanut butter powder (*optional*), and a splash of vanilla to a blender. Puree until incorporated.

Fruit protein smoothie (1 serving): Add 1/4 cup frozen raspberries or frozen strawberries, 3/4 cup frozen blueberries, a handful of spinach, about 1/2 a palm of walnuts, protein powder (again, I use vanilla whey), and about 3/4 cup of organic apple juice to blender. Puree until incorporated. You can play around with different kinds of frozen fruits (pineapple and mango are terrific) or try adding kale instead of spinach and see what you think.

If you make smoothies ahead of time, store them with a lid in the fridge overnight.

Protein Balls

These are a great make-ahead snack to store in the fridge for a quick protein blast.

Blueberry protein ball recipe: Add 1 cup pitted dates to a food processor and pulse about five times. Add 1 cup dried blueberries, 1 cup cashews, 1 cup almonds, zest and juice of 1 lemon, a splash of vanilla, and a pinch of salt and pulse until the mixture is easy to roll into balls. Makes about twenty balls. Store in an airtight container in the fridge for up to two weeks.

Search for more ideas on some of your favorite food websites. Just remember to keep the added sugars low and use less-processed ingredients when possible.

Whole Grains

Quinoa

You can store cooked quinoa in the fridge for several days and either eat it cold or heat it up before adding toppings.

For every cup of quinoa, you'll use two cups of liquid (my preference is chicken stock to add some extra flavor). Place quinoa in a colander with small holes and rinse well. Don't skip this step, because it really helps to get rid of the bitterness. Place quinoa in a saucepan and add liquid. Bring to a boil. Reduce heat, cover, and simmer for fifteen minutes.

Ideas for use: I love to add edamame and cooked shrimp to quinoa with some soy sauce. Add quinoa to salads, as is, for a boost of protein. Use it in a stir-fry instead of rice. Serve leftovers like beef or chicken on top of reheated quinoa.

Whole Wheat Couscous

No need to rinse the couscous before cooking; it doesn't have a bitter flavor like quinoa. Use 1 1/2 cups of water or broth per 1 cup of couscous. Bring liquid to a boil. Pour the couscous into the boiling water or broth, turn off heat, cover, and let sit for five to ten minutes until absorbed. Fluff with a fork. You can easily add lots of goodies (veggies, proteins, healthy fats) to cold couscous for a terrific lunch, dinner, or snack. Store in airtight container in fridge for several days.

Ideas for use: Add leftover beef or chicken and one of your favorite flavoring ingredients, like teriyaki sauce, BBQ sauce, hoisin, tamari, tahini, or homemade vinaigrette. Create a quick salad with cold couscous by adding olive oil, lemon juice, garlic, herbs, veggies (like cucumbers, tomatoes, and green onions), and lean protein, such as cooked shrimp, chicken, or beef.

Rice or Brown Rice

Storing premade rice in the fridge can make for a speedy backup meal, or it can be reheated with some added protein for a fast lunch. It's also great for throwing together stir-fry for dinner.

Follow cooking directions on packaging. Store in airtight container in fridge for several days.

Ideas for use: Add to a stir-fry for a quick lunch or dinner, along with protein, vegetables, and Asian flavoring ingredients, such as soy sauce, sesame oil, etc. Add leftovers to rice and reheat in microwave.

* * *

Experiment with other types of whole grains, like farro or barley, to discover other options.

Vegetables

Kale Salad

I make kale salad every week. It's a nutrition powerhouse, easy to make, and stores beautifully in the fridge for four to five days.

Take one bunch of kale and tear off the leaves (discard the bitter ribs). Place them in a colander. Rinse and dry well. Place kale into a bowl and add just enough olive oil to coat. Massage the hell out of the kale with your fingers for several minutes. You want it to look like you reduced the amount of kale by close to half. This *greatly* reduces the bitterness and is a step that shouldn't be skipped. Add seasonal fruit. My favorites are sliced strawberries or diced mango in the spring and summer, and blueberries and/or sliced apples in the winter. You can experiment with anything you like. Sprinkle in some dried cranberries and chopped walnuts along with goat cheese (I adore honey goat cheese for a little extra sweetness) and a touch of agave nectar. This salad is delicious, ultra-nutritious, and super simple to make.

Don't discount kale until you try it different ways. I

thought I didn't like it for the longest time, but once I started using the massage technique, I never looked back. And boy do I get compliments on this salad whenever I make it for guests.

Note: Don't discard leftover vegetables. They can often be reheated for a delicious side dish for lunch or a healthy snack.

Cauliflower Rice

This is another favorite of mine, as it's easy to reheat in the microwave and serve with leftover protein for lunch or dinner.

Grate one head of cauliflower on larger holes of a box grater (mind your fingers) or in the food processor. You want it to look like snowflakes. Add two tablespoons olive oil and one tablespoon toasted sesame oil to a wok or large skillet over medium-high heat. Add one cup of onions and several cloves of minced garlic, and sauté for about five minutes. Add grated cauliflower and mix well. Cook over medium-high heat for about seven minutes, stirring frequently. Add half a cup water and cover pan. Simmer for five minutes. Remove cover and add soy sauce (*optional*). Let cook another minute. Store in airtight container in fridge for several days.

Ideas for use: Add warm or cold, cooked, sliced steak or chicken to reheated cauliflower rice. Use it in place of rice in a stir-fry.

Oven-Roasted Chickpeas

Rinse a can of chickpeas in a colander and dry with paper towels. Place on rimmed baking sheet. Add enough olive oil to coat, along with spices, such as garlic powder, onion powder, chili powder, or cumin; consider sriracha for a real kick. Bake at 450 degrees for thirty-five to forty minutes until chickpeas get crunchy, mixing a few times while cooking. Store in an airtight container at room temperature for up to five days.

Ideas for use: Great for snacking. Add to salad for extra crunch, some additional protein, and lots of fiber.

I love to experiment with different flavors when I make these.

Spices

Spices are a fantastic way to add lots of flavor with little to no extra calories. And they can even contain lots of nutrients on their own. Keeping premade spice mixes around can be a lifesaver when creating fast or backup meals.

Making your own seasoning mixes is incredibly easy and preferable to buying store-bought mixes, which may contain additives and preservatives. These take no more than a few minutes to put together and add tons of flavor. Plus, you know they're all natural because you made them yourself. They're fast and store in the pantry for a long time. Find recipes online for different types of seasoning mixes, such as Southwest, Italian, Creole, or taco and use them to throw together super quick chicken, meat, fish, and pork dishes.

My favorite spice mixes to make and keep on hand:

Emeril's Essence (my personal favorite and one you'll always find in my pantry): www.foodnetwork.com/recipes/emeril-lagasse/emerils-essence-3645101

Fuego Spice Mix: www.food.com/recipe/fuego-spice-mix-24301

Here's a great website for finding additional spice mixes: www.allrecipes.com/recipes/16328/ingredients/herbs-and-spices/homemade-spice-blends/

Homemade Dressing

I always keep homemade salad dressing in my refrigerator or find simple recipes to create them from scratch in a hurry. They are a much better option than store-bought and take very little time to make. They're easy to prepare, and when you go to eat a salad for lunch or dinner, you'll have peace of mind knowing that a better salad dressing already awaits you in the fridge. Mix simple ingredients either in a food processor, small bowl, or glass jar, and they'll keep in the refrigerator for weeks.

My favorite is a simple vinaigrette, and you'll always find it in my fridge.

Add one clove of garlic to a food processor or blender, and turn on to crush. Add one teaspoon Dijon mustard, one tablespoon sugar, one teaspoon salt, a few grinds of fresh black pepper, and half a cup of red wine vinegar. Turn on processor or blender, and while it's mixing use the feed tube to slowly add in one cup of canola oil. Stores in refrigerator for up to a month.

Search for salad dressing recipes on your favorite food websites. Be sure to make them using mostly whole food ingredients.

Soups

Make soups ahead of time, and you'll be able to put together a fast lunch or dinner. Add an easy side salad, and you're good to go.

Pizza

You might be surprised at how easy it is to make homemade pizza dough. I love to make one out of whole wheat flour and store extra in the freezer. Then I can pull the dough out for one of my weekly meals. The hands-on time is only a few minutes, though the time for rising is usually more than an hour total.

Keep some form of cheese on hand, and you can create a pizza with leftover ingredients like tomatoes, mushrooms, and black olives with the cooked chicken, shrimp, or sausages you made earlier—all without having to make a run to the market. The pizza dough stores well in the freezer, and all you have to do is let it thaw in the fridge overnight.

Keep an eye out for recipes you've either made or are planning to make, and see if any component can be made ahead of time (maybe even cooked once and used twice).

Sign up at lisakschreiber.com for free videos of super simple vegetable recipes and fast, make-ahead meals.

Habit-Based Exercise for Making Foods Ahead (*Optional*)

Week 1 and beyond: Precook at least one protein and one vegetable (and an optional carb) from above (or one of your own) one day this week. Consume for lunch, snack, or as a backup meal (more on that in the next chapter). For example, if you make kale salad, baked chicken, and hard-boiled eggs, you can eat the chicken on the kale salad or on a bed of spinach (with sliced hard-boiled eggs), or put it in a wrap or quesadilla. Or you can make a quick chicken salad or egg salad and place on crackers for a snack and eat the kale as a side veggie. This way you're balancing your meals a little better. Play around with this if you want more variety.

Checklist for Making Foods Ahead (Optional)

Add a checkmark for each time you successfully complete the action. Add an X for when you don't. *No judgment.* It's just a mark.

Week	1	2	3	4	5	6	7
Precook one protein, veggie, and/or optional carb.							

Precooking foods when you have spare time can save you time and frustration on the back end, and it can provide you with some fabulous options for lunches, snacks, and quick dinners. And while it's not the be-all, end-all solution to your meal-planning conundrum, it can go a long way toward having more nutritious options readily available and making meals come together quickly.

You're well on your way to becoming master of your meal-planning domain. Having said that, though, mistakes happen, and things do go awry in the kitchen sometimes. So the next chapter will focus on using ingredients from your well-stocked kitchen to prepare backup meals, just in case. You'll learn to laugh it off and move on.

Chapter 10

CONCOCT BACKUP MEALS WORTHY OF A MAGAZINE COVER

I wish my stove came with a Save As button like Word has. That way I could experiment with my cooking and not fear ruining my dinner.

—Jarod Kintz

I cook a lot—usually six and often seven nights a week. I have for many, many years. So I consider myself somewhat seasoned in the cooking department. And I've made my favorite meatloaf recipe dozens upon dozens of times. But I made a rookie mistake one night when we were having my sister-in-law and brother-in-law for dinner. My hands were a little damp, and I didn't want to reach into the salt dish with my fingers to sprinkle some salt into the meatloaf mixture. Instead, I tried to carefully wave the salt over the meat. Before I knew it, about a quarter cup of the salt ended up in the meatloaf mixture! I scurried to scoop out as much as I could and cooked it anyway. My dear, sweet brother-in-law loaded his plate with ketchup and continued eating like nothing was wrong, but about two bites into the meal, I almost gagged. It was like taking a big gulp out of the Atlantic Ocean. Yuck! After muttering under my breath for a few minutes, I pulled out my backup meal ingredients and a new, less salty dinner was ready in fifteen minutes. We still joke about the debacle today. Why take yourself so seriously?

Another time, as I was getting ready to cook a Miso Chicken recipe for dinner, I realized that the recipe called for marinating the chicken for one hour. At this point, it was getting late, and I didn't want to wait that long to eat. So I scanned my "cookbook" for other chicken recipes and found several that I could use instead. And because my kitchen is always well stocked, I had the ingredients in my fridge and pantry to make a different meal.

Things often go wrong if you're unprepared in the meal-planning department, but even if you've planned to perfection, as Forrest Gump says, "Shit happens." That's when backup meals are incredibly helpful.

You can also use backup meals when you plan not to plan, meaning that even if you don't make time to plan one of your weekly menus, these backup meals can still be a much healthier alternative to eating out.

By the end of this chapter, you'll be able to create backup meals on the fly with items you already have in your well-stocked kitchen. If one of your recipes fails, if you forgot to make something ahead, or if you just decide you don't feel like making the meal you chose, you'll be prepared.

Backup meals are meant to be just that—backups for when one of your meals doesn't work out. They are also handy when you're short on time but don't want to run out and grab an unhealthy meal. And they make fantastic lunches. Backups should take no more than fifteen minutes or so to prepare. You've probably already spent time making one meal that didn't work out, and I doubt you'll want to spend thirty more minutes preparing another. Backup meals should be meals you can make with confidence (i.e. you've made it or something similar before and know it will turn out). They should be easy to make and not at all time consuming. Otherwise, you'll be more likely to say "screw it" and order in or make another fast food run. I'll give you some examples of backup meals I make in our house and offer ideas on how to come up with your own.

Don't fear imperfection. We all make mistakes. And kitchen mistakes are not costly ones (short of burning the thing down). So do not be scared to try. The more you try, the more confident you'll become, and mistakes will be few and far between.

Besides, many of you might already be experts at backup meals; you just don't know it. By not planning your meals, you're probably already pretty good at keeping frozen or ultraprocessed foods on hand for last-minute meals. I'd like to help you tweak those ideas so that what's waiting for you is a bit healthier.

Suggestions for Creating Backup Meals

Step 1   Take stock.

Step 2   Figure out what you're going to cook:

- Search your "cookbook."
- Peruse websites.
- Use flavor profiles and wing it.
- Get creative with your precooked foods.
- Follow meal formulas.
- Play around with my backup ideas.

Step 1: Take Stock

What's in your fridge and pantry that isn't earmarked for another recipe, or do you have enough of those ingredients that you can use the extra? Remember, things like canned beans, leftover beef from dinner the night before, frozen vegetables, eggs, or something you premade are all possibilities.

Step 2: Figure Out What You're Going to Cook

The following are methods I use to come up with recipes after I take stock of what I have on hand.

Search Your "Cookbook"

Once you've taken stock, your first step is to scan your "cookbook" for recipes you could make with what you have. My general rule of thumb is that if you have 80 percent of the ingredients, you can most likely make the meal. Also, check for recipes in different sections. For example, if you have chicken you can use, perhaps that can be substituted in a pork recipe. Starting with your "cookbook" allows you to use a recipe you've made before. If you alter the recipe slightly, it probably won't make that much difference, and you might even create an entirely new dish you can use later. If you substitute one protein for another, make sure it's cooked to a safe temperature.

If you do decide to use a recipe from your "cookbook," make sure the cook time isn't excessive. You probably don't want to spend a lot of time cooking a second meal if you're already behind schedule and in a hurry.

Peruse Websites

Take a look at websites that let you search by ingredient. Use websites like www.myfridgefood.com, www.bigoven.com/recipes/leftover, www.supercook.com/#/recipes, www.recipeland.com/recipes/by_ingredient, or www.recipepuppy.com. You can input ingredients you already have and generate meal ideas. These sites are fantastic at providing meal ideas with few ingredients, and you know you will already have most of them on hand because you've typed them in. With your well-stocked kitchen, you'll very likely have the rest of the ingredients as well.

Again, if you decide to use a recipe from one of these websites, make sure the cook time isn't excessive. And if you find a new "keeper" recipe in the process, be sure to add it to your "cookbook."

Use Flavor Profiles and Wing It

Take one of the flavor ideas below and be a visionary. With your well-stocked kitchen, you are likely to have a lot of these flavors in your fridge and pantry. And if you're unsure what to do, go back to chapter 5 for ideas on combining flavors.

Asian Flavors

Soy sauce	Fish sauce
Hoisin sauce	Wasabi
Sweet and sour sauces	Garlic
Green onions	Ginger
Lemon juice	Sesame oil

Italian Flavors

Olive oil	Mozzarella and
Garlic	parmesan cheeses
Onions	Oregano
Pizza flavors/sauces	Basil
	Thyme

Greek Flavors

Olive oil	Cucumbers
Feta cheese	Greek yogurt
Pine nuts	Dill
Lemon juice	Red onion

BBQ Flavors

Ketchup	Chili powder
Mustard	Cumin
Onions	Cayenne
Vinegar	Worcestershire sauce

Mexican Flavors

Cumin

Chili powder

Chipotle powder

Coriander

Paprika

Chipotles in adobo

Cilantro

Lime

BALANCED MEALS

Remember to balance your meals with lean protein, veggies, and healthy fats as much as possible.

Indian Flavors

Curry powder

Turmeric

Lemon or lime juice

Yogurt

Get Creative with Your Precooked Foods

Your premade ingredients will come in super handy for backup meals. Follow some of my "ideas for use" with your precooked foods in chapter 9 to create super simple dishes if your first attempt is a flop or if you just need to create a spur-of-the-moment dinner.

Follow Meal Formulas

Try using the formula in chapter 6 to create balanced backup meals. I realize you might not have food from all the categories, but it's a starting place toward a balanced meal.

Protein/Main Dish	Vegetable	High-Fiber Carb (Optional)
Chicken	Brussels Sprouts	Quinoa
Beef	Broccoli or Cauliflower	Whole Wheat Couscous
Pork	Leafy Green Veggie (Kale, Lettuce, Etc.)	Beans
Lamb	Squash/Zucchini	Whole Wheat Bread
Fish	Green Beans (or Edamame)	Farrow
Beans, Legumes	Peppers	Brown Rice
Eggs	Carrots	Whole Grain Pasta
Shrimp	Mushrooms	Bulgur
	Tomatoes	Barley
	Asparagus	Corn
		Potato or sweet potato

Play Around with My Backup Ideas

I will tell you that because of my meal-planning system and the length of time I've been cooking, it's very rare that I make backup meals due to failed first attempts. I use them more for lunch ideas or when I need to get food on the table in a hurry and forgot to prepare something ahead of time. I find it incredibly satisfying to look in the fridge or pantry and find I have all the ingredients I need to throw together a nutritious meal at any time of the day.

My Balanced Backup Meal Ideas

The Big Salad

I often put together a quick lunch by using things I usually have in my fridge and pantry, such as spinach, tomatoes, sunflower seeds, dried cranberries, leftover chicken from the night before (or premade, diced chicken I keep in the fridge), and my convenient, homemade salad dressing. It takes less than five minutes to pull together this nutrient powerhouse of a meal. You can do the same by taking some of your premade items, like shrimp or chicken, and placing them on a bed of lettuce, spinach, or kale.

Here's a pic of a quick meal I threw together using ingredients in my fridge and pantry: spinach with already prepared chicken, dried cranberries, sunflower seeds, tomatoes, and a homemade vinaigrette

Seasoned Protein

Sprinkle one of your homemade seasoning mixes on a piece of chicken, meat, or fish and bake, grill, or pan-sear it. Find a recipe, with ingredients you already have, for a simple pan sauce to go on top. Add a veggie, such as salad, as a side. Or skip the pan sauce and put the protein on a bed of spinach, lettuce, or even sautéed zoodles or cauliflower rice.

Stir-Fries

Use pantry essentials (or refrigerated, leftover whole grains), such as quinoa, rice, or pasta, to quickly pull together a stir-fry option. Add protein, like chicken, beef, or shrimp, and veggies. Try using Asian flavors to enhance the dish.

Whole Grain and Protein

Cook quinoa, couscous, or rice—or use precooked if you have them in the fridge—and add veggies, like edamame. Then add lean protein, such as frozen fish that you can cook in twenty minutes or less, or already prepared chicken or beef and a flavoring or two, like soy sauce or tamari.

Quesadillas

I usually keep whole wheat flour tortillas and cheddar cheese in the fridge for such an occasion, and you can add any vegetables or leftover meats you want. You can easily make these for lunch in minutes as well.

Sandwiches or Wraps

Make egg salad sandwiches, or if you have premade chicken in the fridge, you can make chicken salad sandwiches (see chapter 9 for quick recipes). Or, take leftovers or premade chicken or beef and create a sammy or a delicious wrap. Be sure to add veggies if you've got them.

Breakfast

Most of us have eggs and some kind of bread, so why not make breakfast for dinner? Breakfast is my husband's favorite meal, and he loves when I make it for dinner.

- Make your own breakfast sandwiches by scrambling (or frying) eggs, adding cheese, tomatoes, and avocados, and placing it all on 100 percent whole grain English muffins.
- Throw together an omelet (a great way to get in some extra veggies) or even a simple frittata by sautéing vegetables, covering them with an egg mixture, and then baking them in the oven to finish.
- Make a simple egg scramble by adding one or more of your precooked proteins, along with some fresh veggies, to eggs that have been partially scrambled. Then finish cooking until the eggs are to your liking. Serve with a salad and you've got a full meal.

When all else fails, or if you're short on time, who doesn't like bacon and eggs?

Pasta

Cook pasta (preferably whole grain) and add olive oil and parmesan cheese (and maybe herbs like fresh or dried chives). You can also add leftover veggies and some kind of protein to make it a more complete meal and then toss with homemade vinaigrette or marinara.

Frozen Fish

I always keep some kind of fish in the freezer. It's easy to coat frozen fish with olive oil, salt, pepper, and dried or fresh dill weed and bake for twenty to twenty-five minutes. And, fish makes for an incredibly low-maintenance, high-protein source.

Leftovers

Recreate or revitalize leftovers. You could add pantry staples like quinoa, rice, or couscous to leftovers or make sandwiches or quesadillas with leftovers and other simple ingredients.

Salsas

Throw together a quick guacamole salsa by chopping avocados, diced fresh tomatoes, onions, cilantro, salt, pepper, and lemon juice. Or make homemade guacamole by combining diced avocados, diced red onions, lemon juice, garlic, hot sauce, salt, and pepper. Use these to top the premade oven-roasted chicken or steak that's sitting in your fridge for an easy, balanced meal. Or add them to a piece of chicken or beef that you've seasoned with one of your premade spice mixes and grilled, broiled, or baked.

Roasted Veggies

Roasting fresh veggies is a fantastic way to take advantage of what's in season. Because it's such an easy method—not to mention so nutritious—I highly recommend experimenting with this one. These make for simple go-to sides, can be thrown together in minutes, and require few ingredients and little prep time. Try any vegetable and any spice you like.

- Roast broccoli with garlic, olive oil, salt, and pepper at 425 degrees for twenty-five minutes. Add lemon zest, lemon juice, toasted pine nuts, and some parmesan cheese. This is one of Ina Garten's recipes that I make often.
- Thinly slice sweet potatoes, toss in olive oil, salt, and pepper, and cook at 450 degrees for thirty minutes (flipping once).
- Toss fresh green beans with olive oil, salt, pepper, and a little parmesan cheese and bake at 425 for fifteen to twenty minutes (mixing once).
- Rinse frozen edamame in a colander with cold water to thaw. Dry. Place on baking sheet and coat with olive oil. Add salt and parmesan cheese and bake at 400 degrees for fifteen minutes (stirring once).
- Thinly slice summer squash. Place on a baking sheet sprayed with cooking oil, brush each piece with olive oil, add salt, and roast at 375 degrees for twenty minutes (flipping once while cooking).
- Spread broccolini on a baking sheet lined with nonstick foil and coat with olive oil, lemon juice, salt, and pepper. Bake at 350 degrees for fifteen minutes. Delicious! (Note: I highly recommend

using either foil or nonstick foil for the broccolini because I once ruined a pan when I baked broccolini and didn't line the pan.)

- Chop bottoms off brussels sprouts, peel off first layer, and then discard both. Thinly slice the sprouts. Add one tablespoon of butter to a pan. When it's melted, add brussels sprouts, chopped walnuts, dried cranberries, salt, and pepper and cook over medium-low heat for ten minutes, stirring frequently.

- Chop button mushrooms into quarters. Add enough olive oil to coat a sauté pan and place over medium heat. When heated, add mushrooms and sauté for five minutes. Add balsamic vinegar, red pepper flakes, salt, and pepper and sauté for another two to three minutes.

Faux Fries

This is a healthier version of french fries, and it's oh so yummy. You're controlling the type of fat used, so opt for olive, canola, or grapeseed oil. You'll reap the benefits of eating your veggies in an easy, scrumptious, and healthier way.

- Slice russet potatoes or sweet potatoes into thin "fries"; add olive or canola oil, salt, garlic, and/or spices; bake at 425, turning once, until done (about twenty to twenty-five minutes).

- You can do this with butternut squash as well. I love to add sriracha (or chili powder) along with canola oil to butternut squash that I've cut into "fries" and bake them at 425 for twenty minutes (turning once).

You can either put a piece of foil on the baking sheet for easy cleanup, or you can place veggies directly on the pan so they get a little crispier.

Check out lisakschreiber.com for bonus material, including more last-minute or backup meal ideas.

Check out my YouTube channel or go to lisakschreiber.com/about-me to watch videos I made of some of my favorite, super simple veggie recipes.

Getting Creative

Keep your eyes open and you'll see nutritious options everywhere. I was in a hurry the other day, so I stopped into my local market and bought a beautiful salad made with quinoa, corn, and other fixings. And then I realized that there wasn't a lot of protein on it, except for a few beans. When I got home, a quick tour through my fridge revealed a gorgeous piece of leftover chicken from dinner the night before (which was a grilled chicken Caesar salad). The meat made for a fantastic addition to my already prepared salad.

Getting used to cooking with recipes can help you discover what food combinations you like, and that can carry over to your backup meals. For instance, you'll know what to put in that quesadilla (goat cheese, salmon, and fontina cheese) because you've already made recipes with that combination.

Backup meals will give you serious peace of mind and take the pressure off being perfect. And any foods you keep around for backup will most likely get eaten anyway for lunch or if you find yourself short a meal for the week. But when all else fails, call Uber Eats. Or better yet, if you can, walk to a nearby restaurant.

I don't suggest a habit-based exercise for backup meals because I'd rather you spend your time making meal-planning the habit. But rest easier knowing you now have some ideas for putting together nutritious, last-minute meals.

Now that you've got some great options for prep-ahead foods and backup meals, our time together is nearly complete. For now. In the conclusion, I'm going to summarize the habit-based behaviors I've thrown out there for you to consider and bring your meal-planning journey together.

THE END IS JUST THE BEGINNING

*We in the media have been guilty about not doing a better job
of making people understand how really simple cooking is.
We've made everyone feel like they have to be a chef.*

—Ruth Reichl

Are you beginning to feel less overwhelmed about all things food? How are your habits coming along?

Making even small changes to your food lifestyle can seem daunting, so I hope you'll take everything you've learned from *The Meal Deal* and apply the parts of it that fit in with how you live in whatever tiny ways you can. Small changes can lead to massive results down the road.

Here's a quick review of all the habits I've asked you to consider establishing. Please take these at your own pace and don't feel like you have to master everything I'm proposing (and certainly not on my time frame). I'm providing general guidelines to get you started, but only you know what works best for you. It took me years to make these daily and weekly habits, and even now I'm still nowhere near perfect with them. So don't expect a flawless process and embrace small steps.

New Weekly Habits Summary

Week 1

Be mindful at one meal every day.

Start stocking kitchen with green-light foods.

Spend ten minutes searching for new recipes.

Add one new recipe to your "Recipes to Try" folder.

Plan one dinner.

Add items from well-stocked kitchen list.

Add items to your grocery list and get shopping.

Prep and cook meal.

If you have time, precook one protein, veggie, and/or healthy carb.

Week 2

Be mindful at two meals every day.

Plan two dinners this week.

Continue working on your previous weekly habits.

Week 3

Be mindful at every meal.

Plan three dinners this week.

Continue working on your previous weekly habits.

Week 4

Include one veggie every day.

Plan four dinners this week.

Continue working on your previous weekly habits.

Week 5

Include two to three veggies every day. (See if you can work up to four or five fruits and veggies a day.)

Commit to trying one new recipe this week. Add keeper recipe to "cookbook."

Plan five dinners this week.

Continue working on your previous weekly habits.

Week 6

Include a lean protein serving at one meal per day.

Plan five or more dinners this week.

Continue working on your previous weekly habits.

Week 7

Include a lean protein serving at two to three meals per day.

Continue working on your previous weekly habits.

Week 8

Cook with healthier fats, like extra virgin olive oil, at one meal a day.

Continue working on your previous weekly habits.

Week 9

Work up to cooking with healthier fats at three meals a day.

Continue working on your previous weekly habits.

Week 10

Replace one processed carb each week with a whole grain.

Continue working on your previous weekly habits.

Week 11

Work up to replacing processed carbs with a whole grain four to five times a week.

Continue working on your previous weekly habits.

Week 12

Try to balance one meal a day.

Continue working on your previous weekly habits.

Week 13

Try to balance two meals each day.

Continue working on your previous weekly habits.

Week 14

Work up to balancing three meals each day.

Continue working on your previous weekly habits.

Week 15 and Beyond

Be mindful at every meal.

Stock kitchen with green-light foods.

Spend ten minutes searching for new recipes.

Add one new recipe to your "Recipes to Try" folder.

Add items to your grocery list and get shopping.

Prep and cook meals.

If you have time, precook one protein, veggie, and/or healthy carb.

Include two to three veggies every day. (See if you can work up to four or five fruits and veggies a day.)

Include a lean protein serving at two to three meals per day.

Commit to trying one new recipe this week. Add keeper recipe to "cookbook."

Plan five or more dinners this week.

Work up to cooking with healthier fats at three meals a day.

Work up to replacing processed carbs with a whole grain four to five times a week.

Work up to balancing three meals each day.

Now that you've established healthier eating parameters and habits, performed a kitchen makeover and restocked the pantry and fridge, learned where to find recipes and what to look for, created your own magnificent "cookbook," explored what balanced meals look like and why they're important, discovered how to craft fabulous weekly menus you actually look forward to, figured out how to quickly maneuver the market, and learned some food prep techniques (including making some items ahead of time and preparing backup meals, if necessary), you have the skills to be completely autonomous in the kitchen and in control of your food lifestyle. Whew! You've worked hard. I deem you a meal-planning guru. Time to chow down!

You are on your way to becoming a completely self-sufficient healthy eater. Climb on top of the nutritious food tower you've built, declare yourself queen (or king) of the castle, and stand proudly, knowing you have the power to control your food destiny and the skills to eat healthier for a lifetime.

Believe it or not, my goal is for you to be completely autonomous when it comes to meal planning and healthier eating. Having said that, though, every one of us needs some help from time to time. I know that none of this is easy, and I gladly stand by, waiting to help in any way I can. I would love to hear how your healthier-food lifestyle journey is coming along, so check out my website at lisakschreiber.com and leave me feedback or ask me questions. You can also engage on Facebook (The Meal Deal) or Instagram (@themealdealbook) with me and others who are sharing their experiences.

And if I can be of further help, don't hesitate to get in touch for a discovery call. Maybe you'd like more assistance; we could do a live kitchen makeover or plan some menus together. Or perhaps you'd like to dig a little deeper into areas of wellness where you feel stuck and could use a little guidance and accountability. Working one on one to help you get a better hold on your meal-planning and healthier-eating goals would be an honor for me. As I said before, I've been in the dieting, body-image, self-critical trenches along with many of you, and now I'd like to help you build a ladder and climb out.

The good news is you're never doing it wrong. And seeking perfection is a waste of time. The even better news is that small action steps can cascade into much bigger ones down the line. So why not get started?

Your food journey is just that—a journey, not a destination. As your life goes through changes, your food lifestyle will always be a work in progress. So try to simplify the journey and minimize the overwhelm. And instead of needing to have all the answers, be open to allowing eating to evolve along with you. Because we're all works in progress, and our food lives are along for the ride.

FOREVER GRATEFUL

To my GirlPower:

Mom: My soul sister, you have given me the strongest foundation a woman could ask for and an inspiring model to emulate. You were the first person to teach me what love really means through your actions and words.

My fearless little sister, Jill: You have always believed in me, supported me unconditionally, and inspired me through your brave and exceptional actions.

Jenifer F.: You're the best, best friend a girl could ask for. I don't deserve the kind of unwavering support you've always given me, but I sure do appreciate every ounce of it.

Jill B.: My dear friend of over forty years and account-ability partner, your tremendous help in fueling my creative energy has been so far beyond a B+! It would not have been possible to finish this book without your invaluable insights, intense cheerleading, selflessness of time, and calm guidance.

Jaime B.: The strides you helped me take toward finding my place in this world can't be measured, but they are enormous. By urging me to contact my editor that one session, you really were my impetus for seeing this through.

Amanda R.: You took a fearful, unconfident, first-time book author and helped her blossom. Your coaching and talents are beyond compare, and your encouragement pushed me to new heights (and to finally finishing something that meant a lot to me).

For the Boys:

Dad: You departed this world too soon, and I miss you every day. Your hard work, fortitude, and tenacity to finish publishing a work of nonfiction that held so much meaning for you motivated me to keep going. You taught me how to think and the awesome power of kindness and love.

To Scott: My lifeline. Rock. Best friend. Confidant. Your indelible sense of humor makes me laugh every day. Thank you from the bottom of my heart for caring even more about my growth than your own, day in and day out. Your love and respect have been some of the most rewarding things about my life. The privilege of walking through this world with you has been a reward I'm not sure I deserve, but one I definitely never take for granted. Just like your portrayal of the scarecrow in *The Wiz*, your insurmountable courage gives me strength every day.

To Louie F., the most humble man I know, thank you for making my food shine through your stunning photos. I feel honored to have your works of art in this book, and feel even more privileged to call you my friend.

I'm beyond grateful for the countless number of family and friends who have filled my kitchen with meaning, warmth, happiness, love, enthusiasm, laughter, entertainment, and fun over the years. And I look forward to many more years of filling it with good food, kind people, and hopefully, joy.

I'd also like to thank myself for being smart enough to surround myself with the brightest, most empathetic, compassionate, quality people on the planet.

To Precision Nutrition: With the help of coaches, like the incomparable Dr. Krista Scott-Dixon, and through all the training this wonderful organization provided, I began the journey of self-discovery and acceptance. Coach KSD and PN had a profound impact on my personal growth and sparked me to take action and find ways to pass along these lessons to others so we can all learn to be kinder to ourselves and more empathetic to others.

To my new BookLogix family: I thank you for holding my hand and guiding me through the publishing process in such a comforting way. Everyone I've had the privilege of working with at this super professional company has been generous with their time, kind with their words, accommodating, encouraging, full of honesty and integrity, and extremely thorough.

I've spent countless hours trying to build myself up to feeling worthy of introducing myself and this book to the world. All of you I've mentioned are the only reason I was able to get there. Every one of you believed in me long before I started doing the work of believing in myself, and for that, you have my eternal gratitude.

To everyone who buys this book: Thank you for trusting me to be your guide and for sharing your journey toward a healthier lifestyle. You continue to make me a better person every day. I only hope I can give you a fraction of what these incredible people have given me.

BIBLIOGRAPHY

Brown, David. "Study predicts 42 percent of Americans will be obese in 2030." *Washington Post*. May 7, 2012. http://www.washingtonpost.com/national/health-science/study-predicts-42-percent-of-americans-will-be-obese-in-2030/2012/05/07/gIQAeaDL9T_story.html.

Elsevier. "Thirty years of fast food: Greater variety, but more salt, larger portions, and added calories." *ScienceDaily*. February 27, 2019. https://www.sciencedaily.com/releases/2019/02/190227140013.htm.

Gillett, Rachel. "11 ways having too many options is screwing us up." *Business Insider*. November 30, 2016. https://www.businessinsider.com/how-too-many-choices-are-screwing-us-up-2016-11.

Heart.Org Staff. "How much sodium should I eat per day?" American Heart Association. Last reviewed May 23, 2018. https://www.heart.org/en/healthy-living/healthy-eating/eat-smart/sodium/how-much-sodium-should-i-eat-per-day.

Horovitz, Bruce. "Study: 96% of restaurant entrees exceed USDA limits." *ABC News*. May 16, 2012. https://abcnews.go.com/Business/study-96-restaurant-entrees-exceed-usda-limits/story?id=16365110.

Lundell, Dwight. "Heart surgeon speaks out on what

really causes heart disease." Signs of the Times. March 1, 2012. https://www.sott.net/article/242516-Heart-Surgeon-Speaks-Out-On-What-Really-Causes-Heart-Disease.

Martin, Emmie. "90% of Americans don't like to cook— and it's costing them thousands each year." CNBC. September 27, 2017. https://www.cnbc.com/2017/09/27/how-much-americans-waste-on-dining-out.html.

Meyer, Zlati. "Is that my bill? Eating out at full-service restaurants is getting more expensive." USA Today. February 22, 2019. https://www.usatoday.com/story/money/2019/02/22/eating-out-some-restaurants-getting-pricier/2917921002/.

Northwestern University. "America's packaged food supply is ultra-processed: Americans are overexposed to food products that are high in calories, saturated fat, sugar and salt." ScienceDaily. July 25, 2019. https://www.sciencedaily.com/releases/2019/07/190725092534.htm.

Pollan, Michael. In Defense of Food: An Eater's Manifesto. (New York: The Penguin Press, 2008).

Sullivan, M. "Working Families Rely Heavily on 'Convenience' Foods for Dinner, But Save Little Time, Finds UCLA Study." UCLA Newsroom. August 7, 2007. http://newsroom.ucla.edu/portal/ucla/Working-Families-Rely-Heavily-on-8083.aspx.

Wikipedia. S.v. "Food poisoning." Last edited June 29, 2020. https://en.wikipedia.org/wiki/Food_processing.

ABOUT THE AUTHOR

Lisa Kiersky Schreiber is a writer, meal planner, cook, food lover, powerlifter, deep thinker, reader, moderation addict, certified nutrition coach, and lifelong learner. She and her husband live, work, and play in Decatur, Georgia. She studied international relations at Syracuse  University and later received a Precision Nutrition Level 2 certification and a Functional Aging Specialist certification. This is her first book.